SCORE & MANUAL
78F

All for STRINGS

COMPREHENSIVE STRING METHOD ▪ BOOK 1

by Gerald E. Anderson and Robert S. Frost

ALL FOR STRINGS features:

- a unique starting by rote approach
- a thorough and well-founded starting by note approach
- a solid rhythmic foundation and development
- an abundance of technic-building exercises
- a basic introduction to music theory
- a page of scale studies with bowing variations
- photographs showing correct instrument positions and bowgrips
- suggestions for the care and maintenance of each instrument
- a score with an abundance of teaching techniques
- many ensembles (duets, trios and rounds)
- string orchestra arrangements
- solos with piano accompaniment
- color-coded graphics to introduce new material

ALL FOR STRINGS is published for the following instruments:
Violin Viola Cello String Bass

Piano Accompaniment
All piano accompaniments are written in the Conductor's Score. However, the accompaniments are also published in a separate book so that it is available to students for home use and additional practice.

ISBN 0-8497-3226-3

KJOS NEIL A. KJOS MUSIC COMPANY • SAN DIEGO, CALIFORNIA

TABLE OF CONTENTS

STUDENT BOOK PAGE	SCORE PAGE	TITLE
22	72	57. Norwegian Folk Song
		58. Duet in Thirds
23	73	59. Rhythm Teaser
		60.
		61. Bow Divisions
23	74	62. Lightly Row
		63. Pencil Pusher
23	75	64. Jingle Bells
24	76	65. New Notes B and C♯
24	77	66.
		67.
24	78	68. French Folk Song (Duet)
24	79	69. Lift Set Game
25	80	70. New Note D
25	81	71. Tetrachord March
		72. Up the D Major Scale
25	82	73. D Scale Round
		74. Duet Rhythms for the D Major Scale
26	83-85	75. Concert Song
26	86	76. Technic Trainer No. 1
		77. Technic Trainer No. 2
		78. Technic Trainer No. 3
27	87	79. Two of Us
		80. Slow Bows
27	88	81. Bohemian Folk Song
		82. Twinkle, Twinkle, Little Star
27	89	83. Pencil Pusher
28	90	84. O Come, Little Children
28	91	85. D Major Scale in 3
28	92	86. D Scale Waltz
		87. Rhythm Teaser
29	93	88. Position Check
		89. French Folk Song (D Major)
29	94	90. Rhythm Teaser
29	95	91. Tricky Melody
29	96	92. Scotland's Burning
		93. Balance the Scale
30	96	94.
30	97	95.
		96.
		97.
30	98	98. Bow Twister
		99.
30	99	100. Go Tell Aunt Rhodie
31	100	101. It Takes Two
31	101	102. Slur Three
31	102	103. Hickory Dickory Dock
31	103	104. Two Step March
32	104	105. D Arpeggio
		106. Arpeggio March
32	105	107. The Guiding Hand
32	106	108. Solo Time
32	107	109. Pencil Pusher
33	108	110.
		111.
33	109	112. New Notes A, B and C
		113.
33	110	114.
		115. London Bridge
33	111	116. G Major Scale
34	111	117.
34	112	118. Technic Trainer No. 1
		119. Technic Trainer No. 2
		120. Technic Trainer No. 3
34	113	121. Tonic and Dominant Arpeggios
		122. Peter Peter
34	114	123. Reuben and Rachel
		124. Melody for Three Strings
35	115-116	125. Three String Madness
35	117-118	126. Concert Trio
36	119	127.
		128. Czech Folk Song

STUDENT BOOK PAGE	SCORE PAGE	TITLE
36	120	129. She'll Be Comin' 'Round the Mountain
36	121	130. Little Annie
36	122	131. Rhythm Teaser
37	123	132. Long, Long Ago
37	124	133. Theme-Beethoven Violin Concerto
37	125	134. Can-Can
		135.
		136. N. Paganini
38	127	137. Kookaburra
38	128	138. Jolly Old St. Nick
38	129	139. The Old Woman and the Peddler
38	130	140. Rhythm Teaser
39	131	141. New Note F♮
39	132	142.
		143.
		144.
39	133	145. Folk Song
		146. Finger Twisters
40	134	147. Keep the Music Ringing
		148. A Tisket a Tasket
40	135	149. Hi-Lo No. 1
		150. Hi-Lo No. 2
		151. Musical Road Signs
40	136-137	152. Mexican Clapping Song/Oh Where Has My Little Dog Gone
40	138	153. Snake Charmer
		154. Position Check
41	139	155. New Note C♮
41	140	156.
		157. Some Folks Do
		158.
41	141	159. Bow Twister
		160. Technic Trainer
		161. Finger Twister
42	142	162. Canon
42	144	163. French Folk Song (C Major)
		164. Bridge at Avignon
42	145-146	165. There's Music in the Air
42	147	166. Fingering Review
43	148	167. New Notes F♯ and G
43	149	168. New Note A
		169. Technic Trainer
43	150	170. G Major Scale With Broken Thirds
43	151	171. Arpeggio Fun
44	152	172. When Love Is Kind
44	153	173. Saints
44	154-155	174. Skip to My Lou
44	156	175. Shepherd's Hey
45	157	176. New Notes C, D and E (violas and cellos play on their C string)
45	158	177. New Note F
		178.
45	159	179. C Major Scale With Broken Thirds
45	160	180. Arpeggio Fun
46	161-162	181. Duet in Two Keys
46	163-165	182. Theme and Variations
47	166-169	183. Happy Blues
47	170-171	184. Jazz Feature
48	172	TECHNIC DEVELOPMENT 1. D Major Scale 2. D Major Broken Thirds
48	173	3. G Major Scale 4. G Major Broken Thirds 5. C Major Scale
48	174	6. C Major Broken Thirds
INSIDE BACK COVER	175	VIOLIN GLOSSARY
	176	VIOLA GLOSSARY
	177	CELLO GLOSSARY
	178	BASS GLOSSARY
	179	*RECRUITING*
	180	*BIBLIOGRAPHY*

TEACHER: The following introductory letter appears on the first page of every student book.

All for STRINGS
COMPREHENSIVE STRING METHOD • BOOK 1
by Gerald E. Anderson and Robert S. Frost

Dear String Student:

Welcome to the wonderful world of orchestra music!

The moment you pick up your stringed instrument, you will begin an exciting adventure that is filled with challenges and rewards.

Using **ALL FOR STRINGS**, your teacher will help you to develop the skills that will enable you to become a fine string player. If you study carefully and practice regularly, you will quickly discover the joy and satisfaction of playing beautiful music for yourself, your family, your friends or a concert audience.

We hope that **ALL FOR STRINGS** will lead you toward many years of pleasure in beautiful music making.

Best wishes!

Gerald E. Anderson
Robert S. Frost

PARTS OF THE VIOLIN AND VIOLA

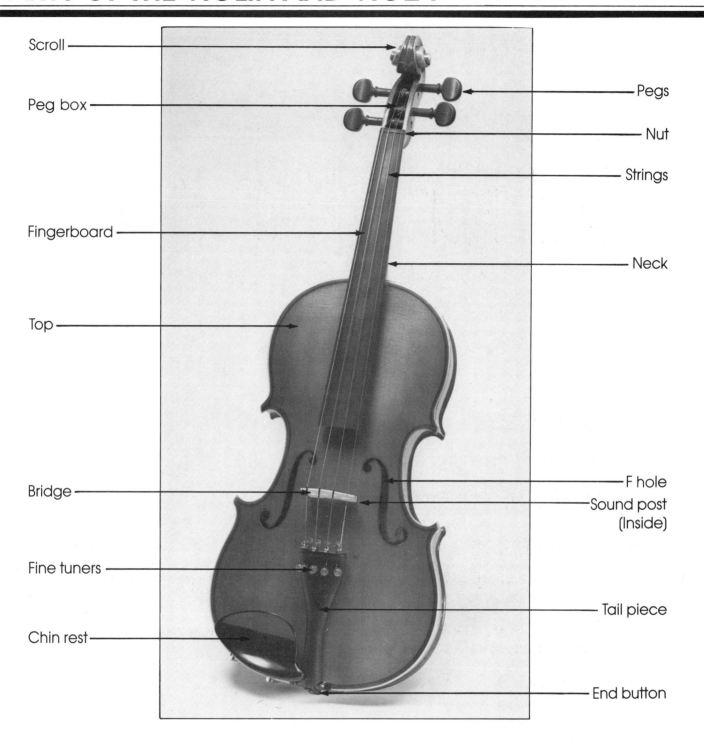

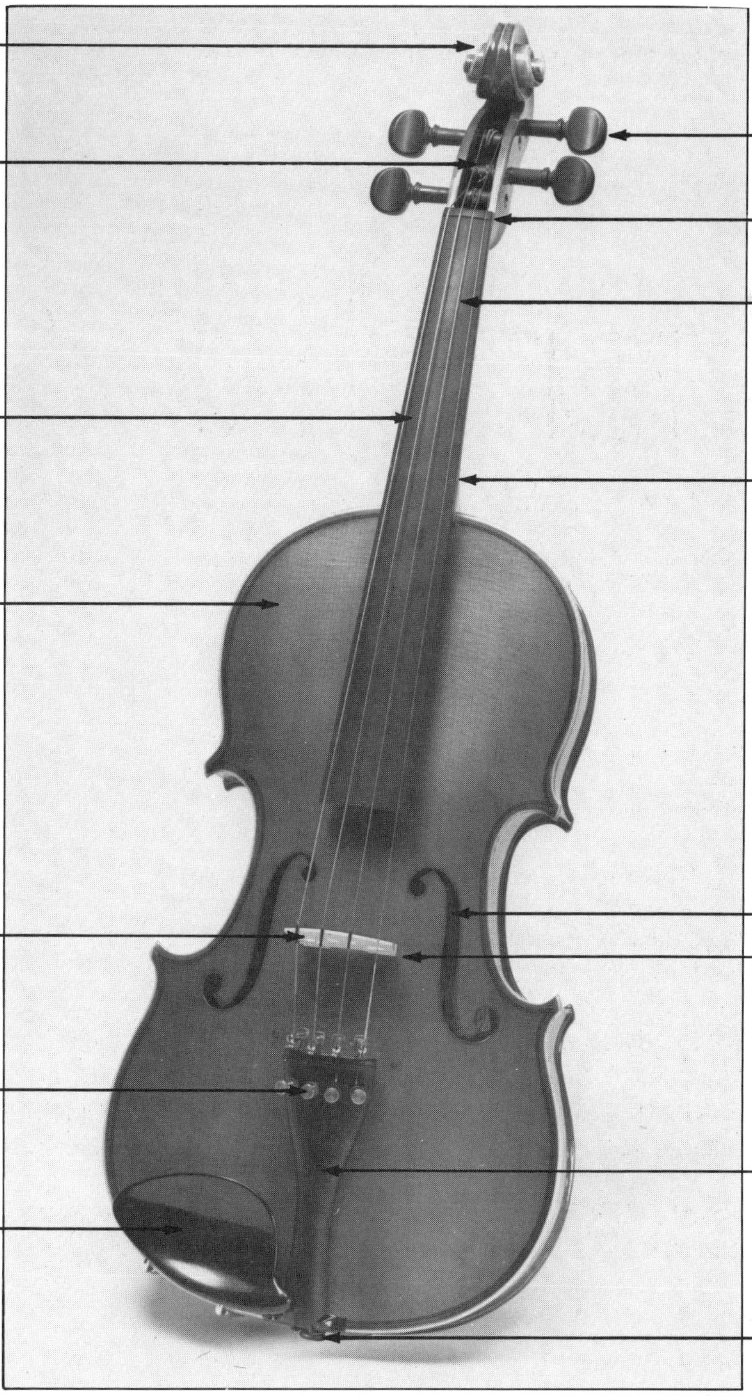

Scroll
Peg box
Fingerboard
Top
Bridge
Fine tuners
Chin rest
Pegs
Nut
Strings
Neck
F hole
Sound post
(Inside)
Tail piece
End button

PARTS OF THE BOW

Tip or Point
Stick
Adjusting screw
Hair
Bow grip
Frog

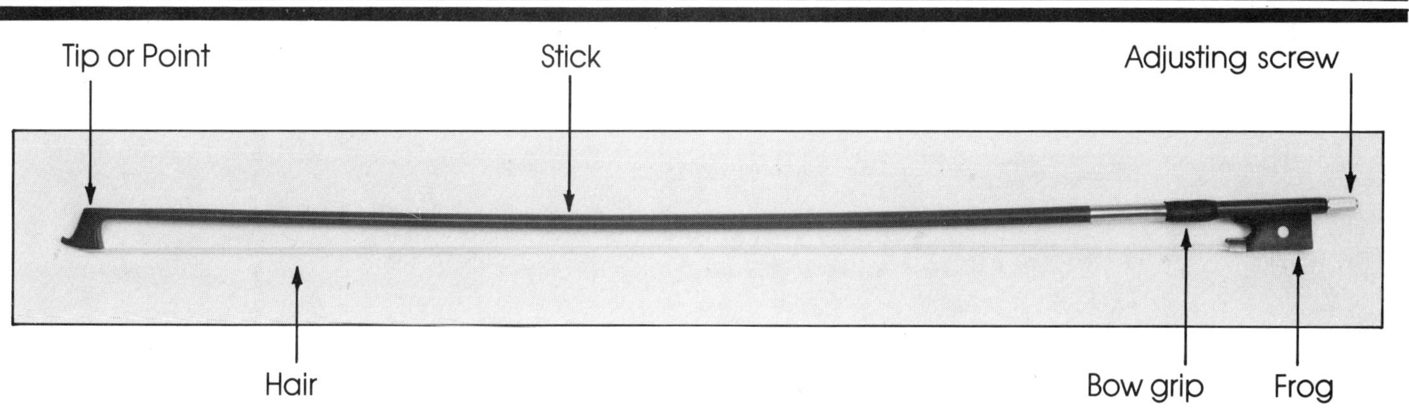

PARTS OF THE CELLO

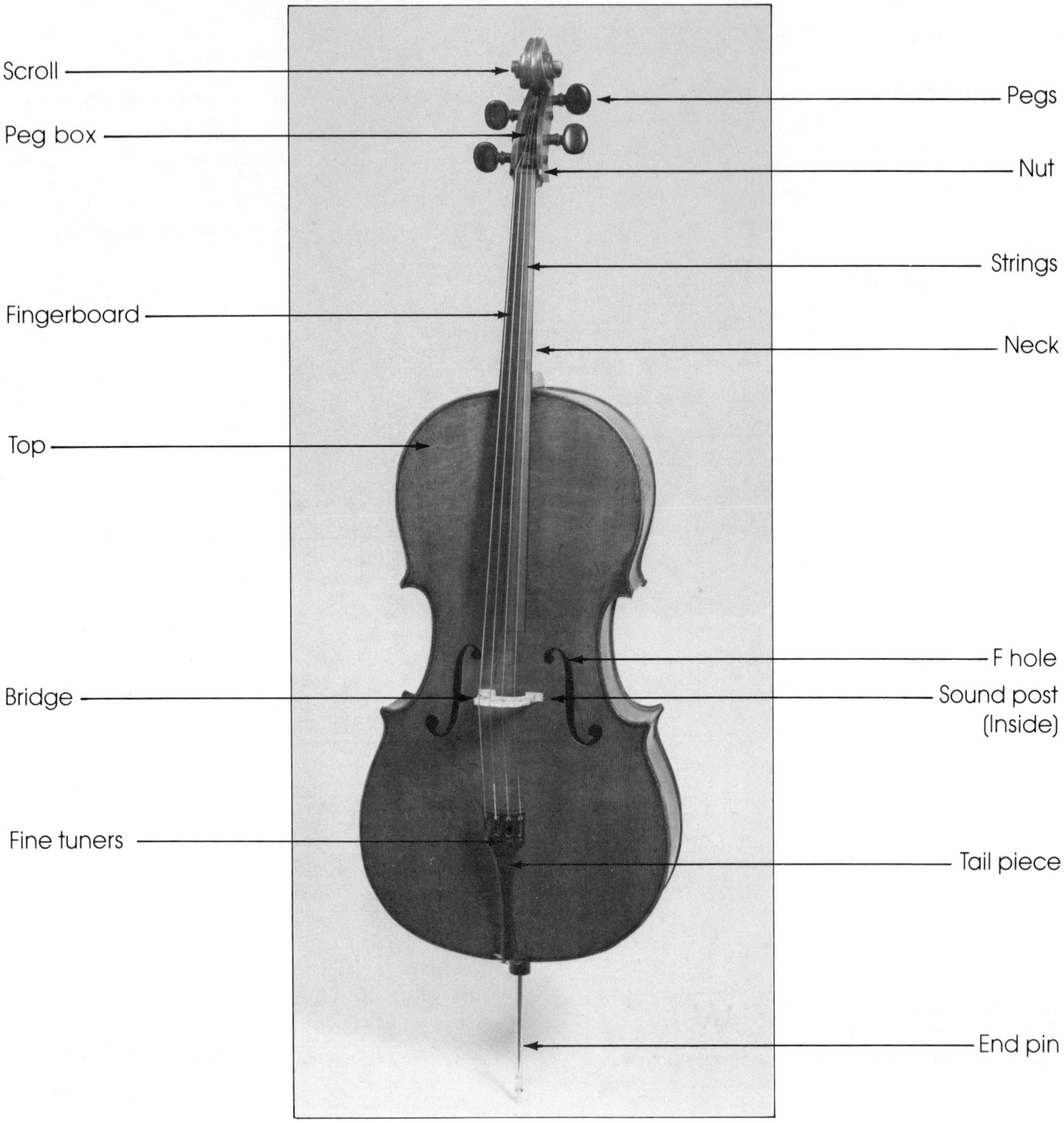

Scroll
Peg box
Pegs
Nut
Strings
Fingerboard
Neck
Top
F hole
Bridge
Sound post
(Inside)
Fine tuners
Tail piece
End pin

PARTS OF THE BOW

Tip or Point
Stick
Adjusting screw
Hair
Bow grip
Frog

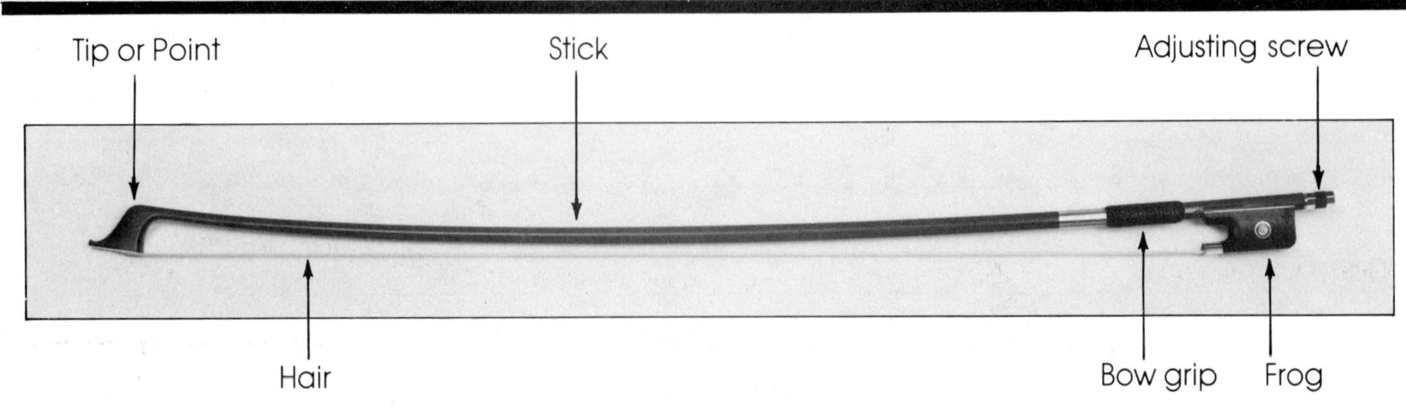

PARTS OF THE STRING BASS

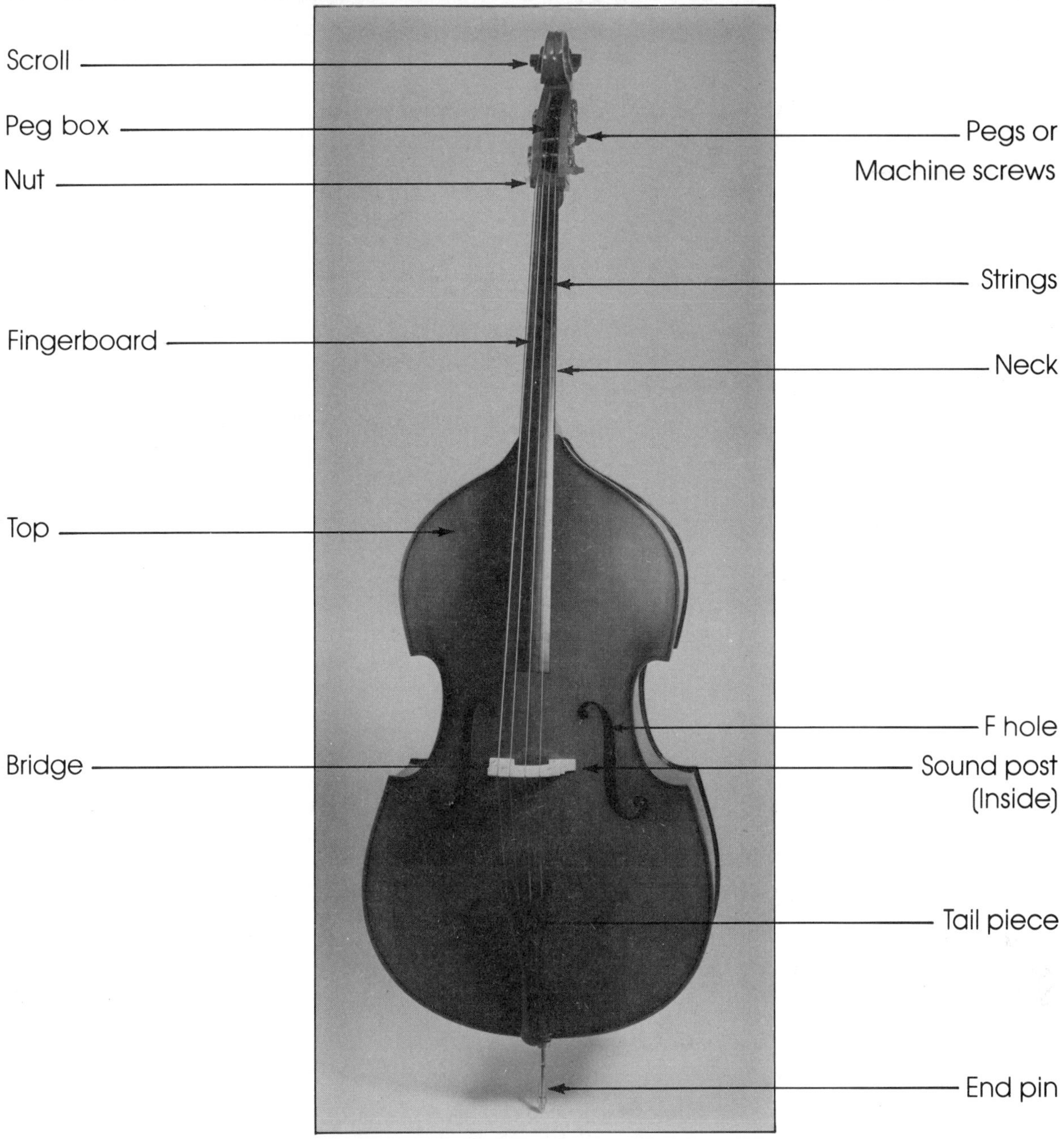

Scroll
Peg box
Nut
Pegs or Machine screws
Strings
Fingerboard
Neck
Top
F hole
Bridge
Sound post (Inside)
Tail piece
End pin

PARTS OF THE BOW

French Bow

Tip or Point
Stick
Adjusting screw
Hair
Bow grip
Frog

German Bow

Tip or Point
Stick
Adjusting screw
Hair
Bow grip
Frog

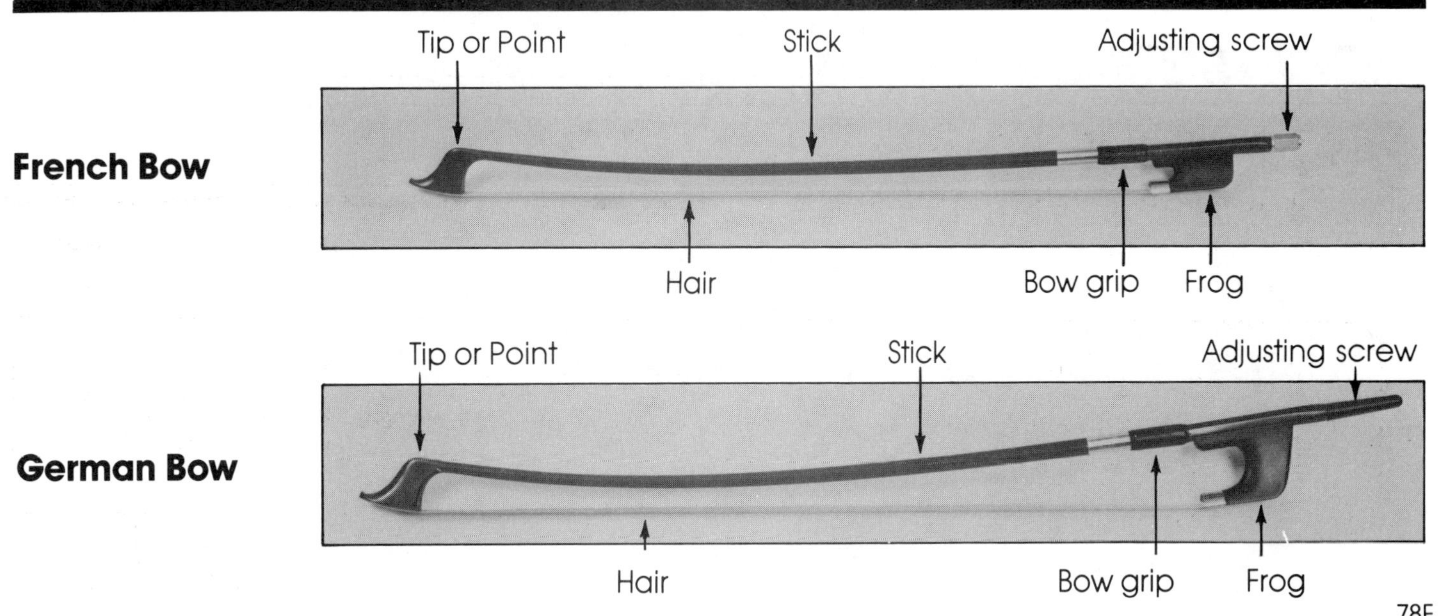

CARE OF THE INSTRUMENT (VIOLIN AND VIOLA)

1. Handle your instrument, bow and case with care. Instruments and bows are made of thin wood, and can break easily. Bumping your instrument, either in or out of the case, may cause it to go out of adjustment.
2. Keep your instrument clean. Each time you finish playing, use a soft cloth to wipe the rosin dust from your instrument, bow stick and strings.
3. When you are not using your instrument, always store it in its case.
4. Before placing your instrument in its case, remove the shoulder rest.
5. When your instrument is in the case, keep the case latched securely.
6. Never put your method book in your case. Placing your book in the case may cause your instrument to break or to go out of adjustment.
7. Do not expose your instrument to excessive heat or cold. Extreme temperatures may cause your instrument to crack.
8. Check your bridge often. If it is not standing straight, ask your teacher to adjust it. Do not adjust it yourself.
9. Do not attempt your own repairs. Only an expert musical instrument repairman has the skill and experience to repair your instrument.
10. Do not let others play your instrument.

CARE OF THE BOW

1. Be careful! Bows break easily. Do not drop your bow or hit it on anything that will cause it to break.
2. Do not touch the hair of your bow. Moisture, perspiration, oil or dirt from your hands, face, or hair will spoil the bow hair.
3. Before you begin to play, tighten your bow with the adjusting screw. Your teacher will show you the correct tension to use.
4. Each time you finish playing, loosen the tension of your bow. Your teacher will show you how much to loosen the bow hair.
5. When you are not using your bow, always store it in the case.
6. Rosin your bow several times each week.

ACCESSORIES

1. Rosin
2. Shoulder rest
3. Soft cloth
4. Extra set of strings
5. Music stand
6. Pitch pipe
7. Music folder

CARE OF THE INSTRUMENT (CELLO AND BASS)

1. Handle your instrument, bow and case with care. Instruments and bows are made of thin wood, and can break easily. Bumping your instrument, either in or out of the case, may cause it to go out of adjustment.
2. Keep your instrument clean. Each time you finish playing, use a soft cloth to wipe the rosin dust from your instrument, bow stick and strings.
3. When you are not using your instrument, always store it in its case.
4. When you unpack your instrument, take the bow out of the (soft) case first. This will prevent you from accidentally breaking the bow, or scraping the instrument.
5. When you pack your instrument, place the bow in the (soft) case last. This will prevent you from accidentally breaking the bow.
6. Store your method book in the pocket provided on the back of your (soft) case.
7. Do not expose your instrument to excessive heat or cold. Extreme temperatures may cause your instrument to crack.
8. Check your bridge often. If it is not standing straight, ask your teacher to adjust it. Do not adjust it yourself.
9. Do not attempt your own repairs. Only an expert musical instrument repairman has the skill and experience to repair your instrument.
10. Do not let others play your instrument.

CARE OF THE BOW

1. Be careful! Bows break easily. Do not drop your bow or hit it on anything that will cause it to break.
2. Do not touch the hair of your bow. Moisture, perspiration, oil or dirt from your hands, face, or hair will spoil the bow hair.
3. Before you begin to play, tighten your bow with the adjusting screw. Your teacher will show you the correct tension to use.
4. Each time you finish playing, loosen the tension of your bow. Your teacher will show you how much to loosen the bow hair.
5. When you are not using your bow, always place it in the (soft) case after you have packed your instrument.
6. Rosin your bow several times each week.

ACCESSORIES

1. Rosin
2. Rock stop (End pin holder)
3. Soft cloth
4. Extra set of strings
5. Music stand
6. Pitch pipe
7. Music folder

PARTS OF THE INSTRUMENT

It is important that students learn the parts of the instrument and bow. You may want to copy student book page 2 and use it for a test. Simply block out the names of the instrument parts and have your students fill in the blanks.

CARE OF THE INSTRUMENT

Suggest that the students wash their hands before playing. Dirt on the instrument and bow will keep them from sounding and looking their best.

The instrument and bow stick can be cleaned with a special string instrument cleaner-polish. This special cleaner-polish will keep the instruments looking new by removing built-up rosin and dirt. Suggest that the students clean their instrument thoroughly once or twice a year. A qualified repairman can also clean the instrument. Students will be proud of a clean and bright looking instrument.

ACCESSORIES

ROSIN
Rosin is generally made in either round or oblong cakes and will melt or become soft if subjected to too much heat. Bass rosin is the softest and is often gummy in consistency. Soft rosins may be used in cool climates and hard rosins in warm climates. Rosins also come in varying degrees of coarseness; amber color being the least coarse and dark colors the most coarse. Younger players most often use the light amber colored rosin. As the student advances, the teacher may suggest using the darker colored rosin as it will help produce a fuller tone.

Violin, viola and cello players should rosin the bow by placing the bow on top of the rosin cake and drawing the bow back and forth across the rosin from frog to tip. A few small back and forth strokes at the frog and tip will deposit a small amount of rosin that can be spread the entire length of the bow. The bass bow is drawn only from frog to tip because the sticky consistency of their rosin would cause the hairs to be pulled out of the bow if pulled back and forth. Stress the importance of wiping the rosin from the top of the instrument, strings and bow stick after each playing session.

ROCK STOPS
Rock stops (end pin rests) are round or square with a non-slip rubber surface to place against the floor. A brass cup on top provides a place to anchor the end pin of the cello or string bass.

CELLO BOARDS
Another alternative is to use cello boards which can be made from a piece of wood ½″ to ¾″ thick, 3″ wide and about 28″ long. A large 2″ diameter hole can be cut near one end and a series of ⅜″ holes drilled at an angle half way through the board at varying distances from the other end. The left leg of the cellist's chair is placed into the large hole and the end pin of the cello is placed into the small hole that would position the instrument at the proper angle for the player.

SHOULDER RESTS

A shoulder rest or pad should be used to fill the space between the top of the left shoulder and the back of the violin or viola and provide a non-slippery surface against which the shoulder can press when holding the instrument. Many different sizes and types of shoulder rests and pads are available. Young students require a smaller pad and may feel more comfortable with a homemade type made from one inch thick foam rubber or sponge covered with a soft material.

PENCIL

You may find it helpful to have the students carry a pencil and small note pad in their cases to record assignments and practice time.

STRINGS

Metal strings with fine tuners are preferred for young players because they hold their pitch better and are easier to tune than gut core strings. Fine tuners MUST be used with metal strings because they do not have the elasticity of gut core strings. A slight turn of the peg will change the pitch of a metal string a great deal. Therefore, it is difficult to turn the peg to the exact place to be in tune. Attaching the string to a fine tuner will allow you to make fine tuning adjustments. Also, metal strings are not as affected by temperature and humidity changes as are gut core strings. These reasons make metal strings with fine tuners the preferred choice or set up for young string students.

Avoid the use of fine tuners for gut core strings. The amount of adjustment needed to tune such a string is greater than is possible with a fine tuner. Also, the tuner will cut into the gut core string causing it to break prematurely.

It is important to select the right size string for a particular size of instrument, in other words, a ¾ size string for a ¾ size instrument.

Metal strings are available in various degrees of loudness. Select a model of string that sounds best on a particular instrument.

FINGERING AIDS

Placing tapes or dots on the fingerboard to help beginning students find the correct finger placement is a widely accepted practice. These tapes or dots should be used only as a rough guide for finger position. They are not a substitute to training the students to listen. After the students have achieved acceptable finger placement, the tapes and dots should be removed. Following is one suggestion for placement of these tapes or dots:

Violin/Viola—1st finger and high 2nd finger
Cello—1st finger and third finger
String Bass—1st finger and 4th finger

A small piece of tape may also be placed on the back of the neck of the cello and bass to show the proper placement for the thumb.

INSTRUMENT SIZES

The importance of each student starting on the correct size of instrument should not be overlooked. Sometimes the family violin is the wrong size for a young beginner. The string pedagogy books listed in the Bibliography on page 180 will give instructions for selecting the correct size instrument for each student.

Figure 1

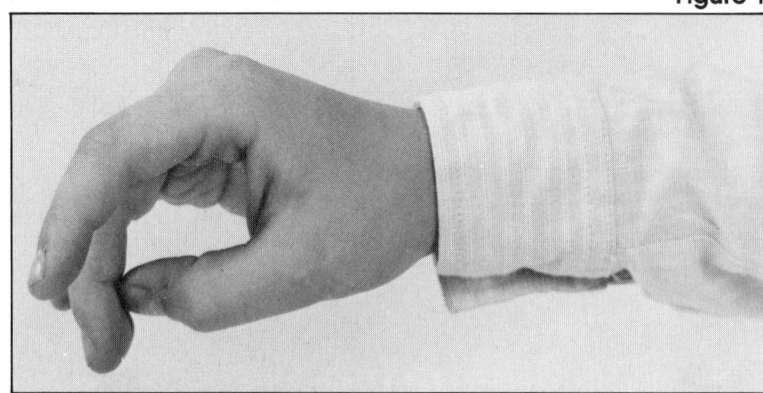

Figure 2

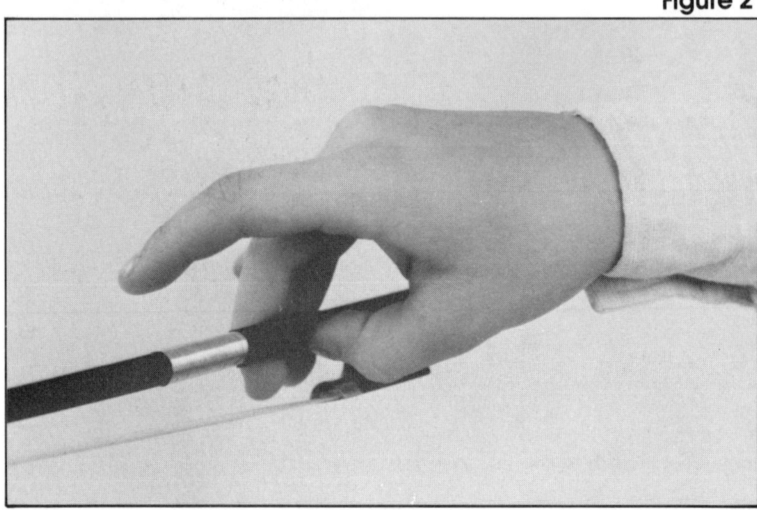

Figure 3

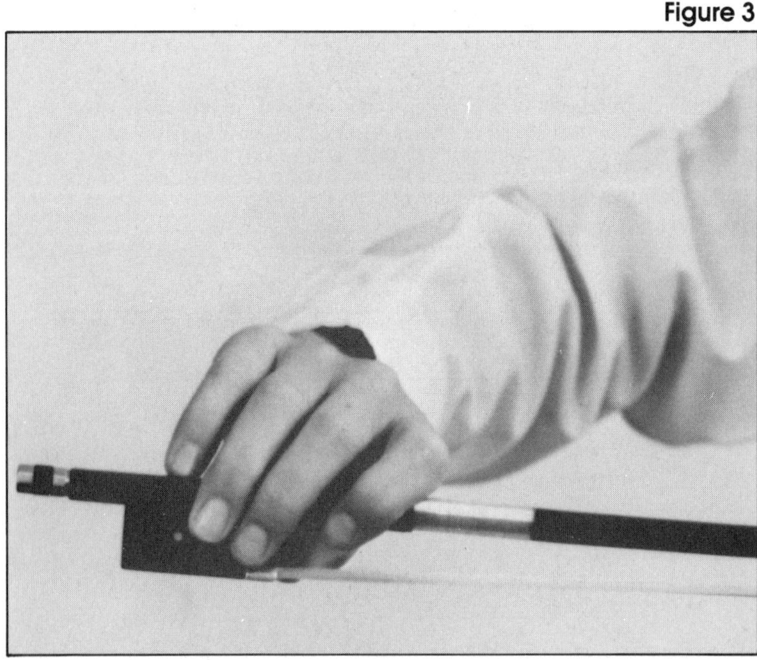

Figure 4

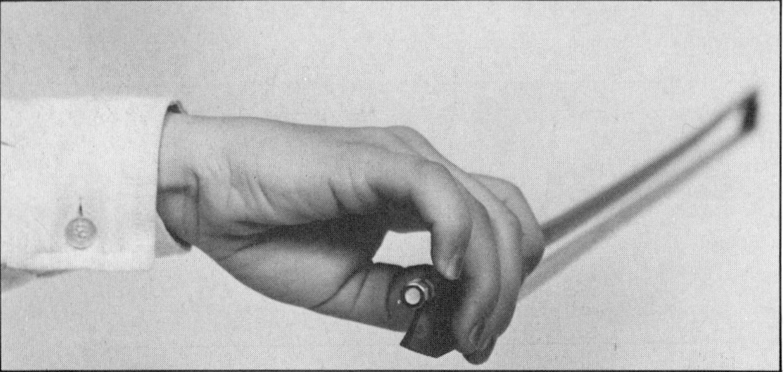

BOW GRIP

1. Make a **circle** with the tip of your thumb on the first joint or crease of your middle finger. **Keep your thumb bent.** See figure 1.
2. a. Holding the middle of your bow (pencil) with your left hand, lift your right hand thumb and place the stick (pencil) on the first joint or crease of your middle finger.
   b. Place the tip of the thumb on the stick next to the frog.
   Keep your circle.
   Keep your thumb bent.
   See figure 2.
3. a. Turn your hand inward or toward the tip of the bow.
   b. Place your index finger between the first and second joints over the stick (pencil).
   See figure 3.
4. Lay your ring finger comfortably over the stick (pencil) on the frog.
   See figure 3.
5. Place the tip of your little finger on the top of the stick (pencil).
   Keep your little finger curved.
   See figures 3 and 4.
6. Check your entire bow grip.
   Reminder: THUMB BENT
   LITTLE FINGER CURVED
   HAND RELAXED
   See figures 3 and 4.

BOWING

1. Place the bow on the string half way between the bridge and the fingerboard.
   See figures 5 and 6.
2. Tilt the bow stick slightly toward the fingerboard (away from the bridge).
   See figures 5 and 6.
3. Press the bow firmly into the string.
4. Move the bow in a straight line with the bridge. Keep the bow at right angles to the string.
5. Raise your wrist slightly at the frog and lower it as you draw closer to the tip.
6. Relax your right shoulder, elbow and wrist.

BOW GRIP EXERCISES

Your teacher will explain how to do these exercises.

1. Pinkie Lifter
2. Flex
3. Wave
4. Teeter-Totter
5. Squeeze-Relax
6. Windshield Wiper
7. Spider
8. Rocket Launch

Violin

INSTRUMENT POSITION

1. Stand or sit with correct posture.
   See figures 5 and 6.
2. Attach the shoulder rest in the proper position on the violin.
3. Place the violin on your left shoulder.
4. Be sure that:
   a. your left shoulder is well under the violin.
   b. the left corner of your chin is in the chinrest so that you are looking straight down the strings.
   c. the violin is tilted slightly to the right.
   d. the violin is parallel to the floor.
   e. the following are in line:
      - nose
      - strings
      - left elbow
      - left foot

   See figures 5 and 6.
5. Relax your left shoulder.

Figure 5

Figure 6

LEFT HAND POSITION

1. Place the first joint of your thumb on the neck.
   See figure 7.
2. Curve your fingers over the fingerboard.
   See figure 7.
3. Adjust your wrist and forearm to form a straight line.
   See figures 5 and 6.
4. Be sure that:
   a. your thumb is relaxed, straight and pointed upwards.
   b. your thumb and first finger are opposite each other.
   c. your wrist is straight.
   d. your fingernails are cut short.
5. Relax your left shoulder.

Figure 7

Figure 1

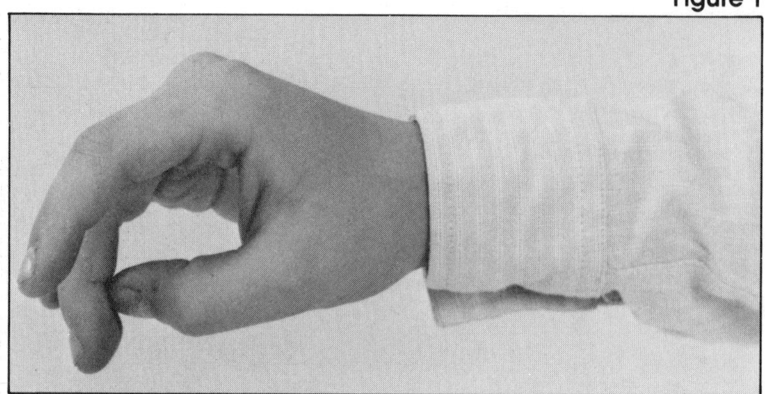

Figure 2

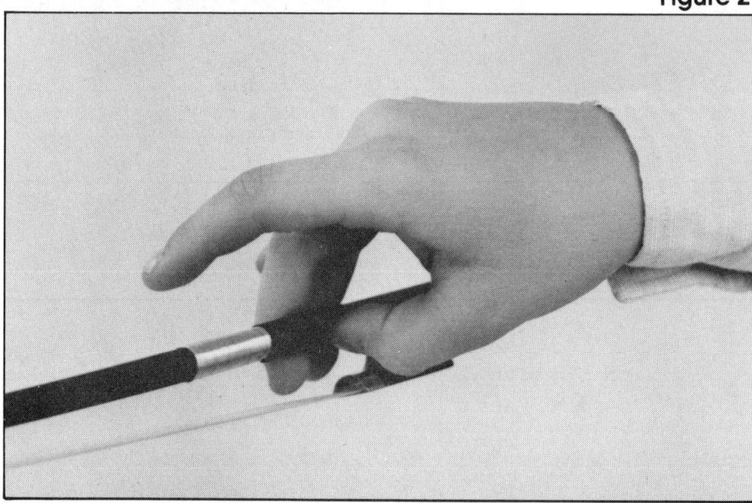

Figure 3

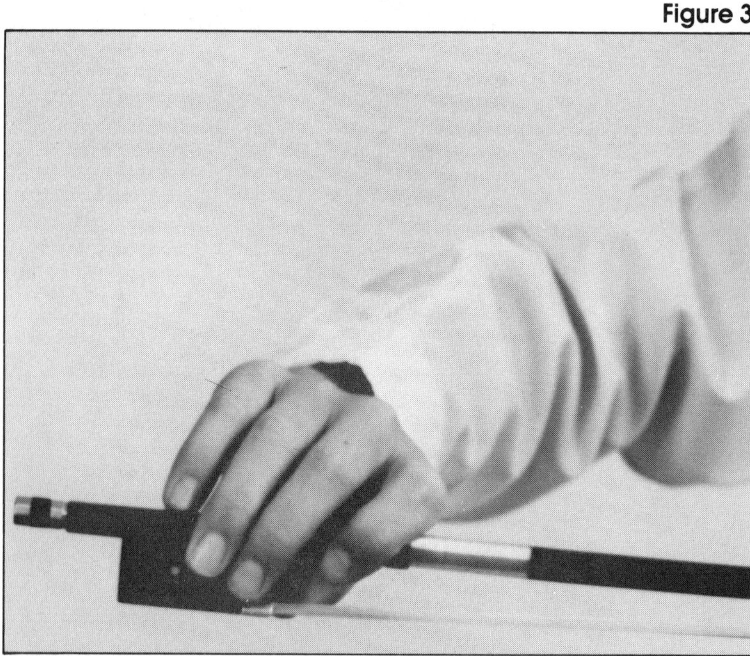

Figure 4

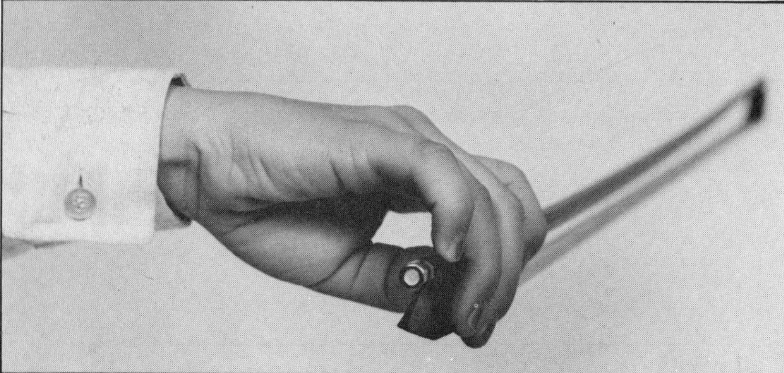

BOW GRIP

1. Make a **circle** with the tip of your thumb on the first joint or crease of your middle finger.
   Keep your thumb bent.
   See figure 1.
2. a. Holding the middle of your bow (pencil) with your left hand, lift your right hand thumb and place the stick (pencil) on the first joint or crease of your middle finger.
   b. Place the tip of the thumb on the stick next to the frog.
   Keep your circle.
   Keep your thumb bent.
   See figure 2.
3. a. Turn your hand inward or toward the tip of the bow.
   b. Place your index finger between the first and second joints over the stick (pencil).
   See figure 3.
4. Lay your ring finger comfortably over the stick (pencil) on the frog.
   See figure 3.
5. Place the tip of your little finger on the top of the stick (pencil).
   Keep your little finger curved.
   See figures 3 and 4.
6. Check your entire bow grip.
   Reminder: THUMB BENT
   LITTLE FINGER CURVED
   HAND RELAXED
   See figures 3 and 4.

BOWING

1. Place the bow on the string half way between the bridge and the fingerboard.
   See figures 5 and 6.
2. Tilt the bow stick slightly toward the fingerboard (away from the bridge).
   See figures 5 and 6.
3. Press the bow firmly into the string.
4. Move the bow in a straight line with the bridge. Keep the bow at right angles to the string.
5. Raise your wrist slightly at the frog and lower it as you draw closer to the tip.
6. Relax your right shoulder, elbow and wrist.

BOW GRIP EXERCISES

Your teacher will explain how to do these exercises.

1. Pinkie Lifter
2. Flex
3. Wave
4. Teeter-Totter
5. Squeeze-Relax
6. Windshield Wiper
7. Spider
8. Rocket Launch

INSTRUMENT POSITION

1. Stand or sit with correct posture.
   See figures 5 and 6.
2. Attach the shoulder rest in the proper position on the viola.
3. Place the viola on your left shoulder.
4. Be sure that:
   a. your left shoulder is well under the viola.
   b. the left corner of your chin is in the chinrest so that you are looking straight down the strings.
   c. the viola is tilted slightly to the right.
   d. the viola is parallel to the floor.
   e. the following are in line:
      - nose
      - strings
      - left elbow
      - left foot

   See figures 5 and 6.
5. Relax your left shoulder.

Figure 5

Figure 6

LEFT HAND POSITION

1. Place the first joint of your thumb on the neck.
   See figure 7.
2. Curve your fingers over the fingerboard.
   See figure 7.
3. Adjust your wrist and forearm to form a straight line.
   See figures 5 and 6.
4. Be sure that:
   a. your thumb is relaxed, straight and pointed upwards.
   b. your thumb and first finger are opposite each other.
   c. your wrist is straight.
   d. your fingernails are cut short.
5. Relax your left shoulder.

Figure 7

Figure 1

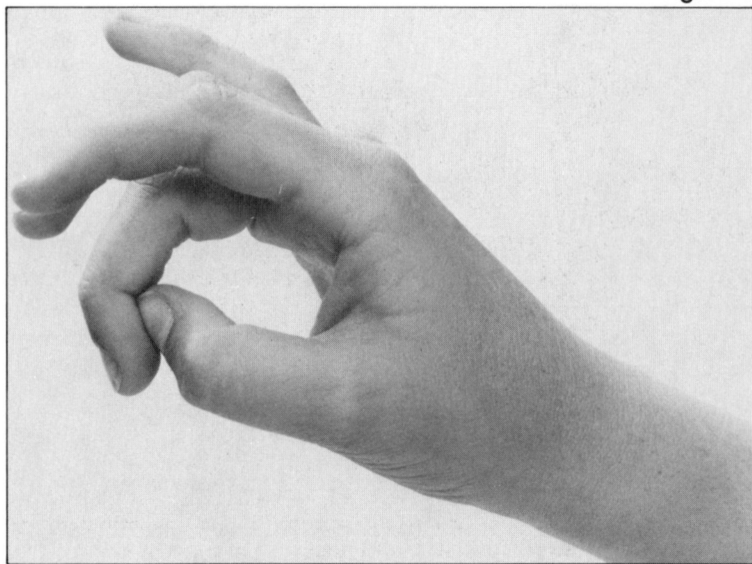

Figure 2

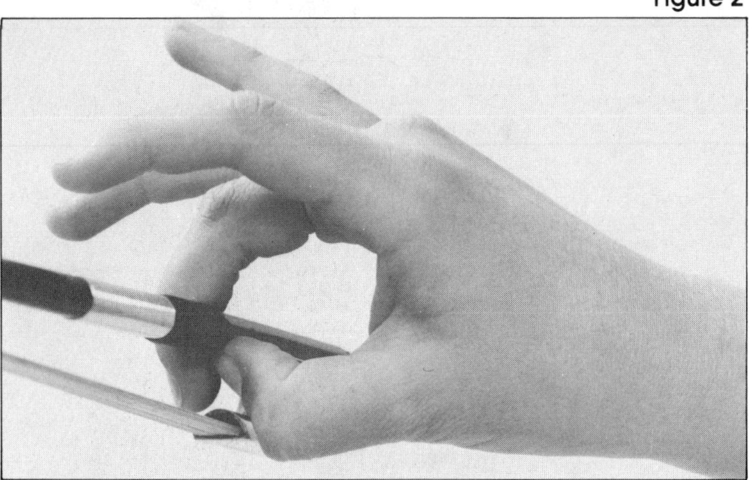

Figure 3

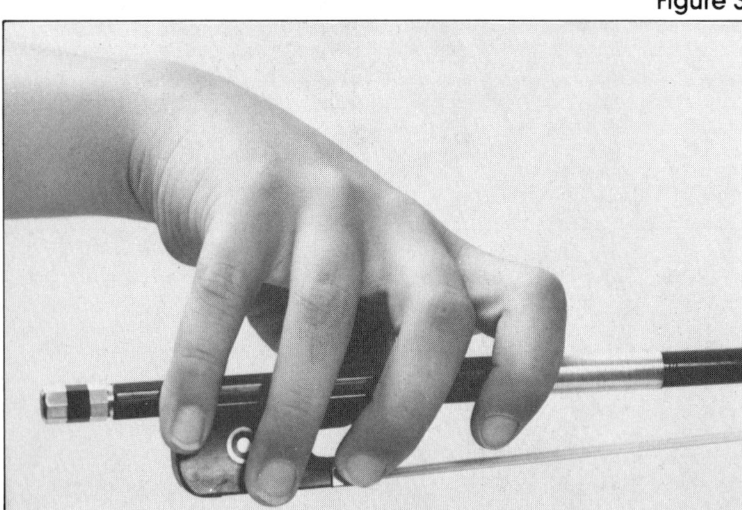

Figure 4

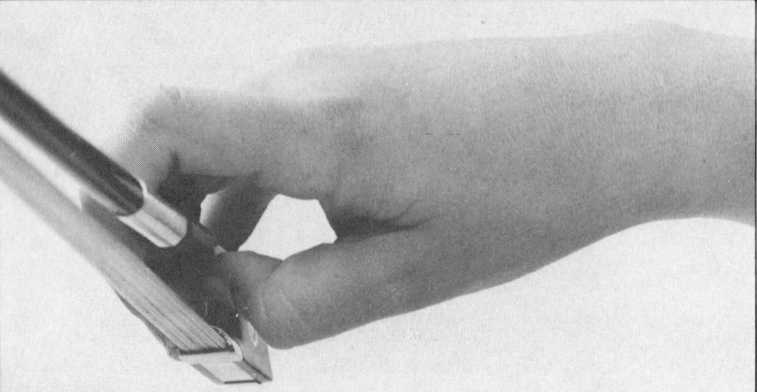

BOW GRIP

1. Make a **circle** with the tip of your thumb on the first joint or crease of your middle finger. **Keep your thumb bent.**
   See figure 1.
2. a. Holding the middle of your bow (pencil) with your left hand, lift your right hand thumb and place the stick (pencil) on the first joint or crease of your middle finger.
   b. Place the tip of the thumb on the stick (pencil) next to the frog.
   Keep your circle.
   Keep your thumb bent.
   See figure 2.
3. a. Turn your hand inward or toward the tip of the bow.
   b. Place your index finger at the first joint over the stick (pencil).
   See figure 3.
4. Lay your ring finger comfortably over the stick (pencil) on the frog.
   See figure 3.
5. Place your little finger at the first joint over the stick (pencil).
   Keep your little finger curved.
   See figures 3 and 4.
6. Check your entire bow grip.
   Reminder: THUMB BENT
   FINGERS CURVED OVER THE STICK
   HAND RELAXED
   See figures 3 and 4.

BOWING

1. Place the bow on the string half way between the bridge and the fingerboard.
   See figure 6.
2. Tilt the bow stick slightly toward the fingerboard (away from the bridge).
   See figure 6.
3. Press the bow firmly into the string.
4. Move the bow in a straight line with the bridge. Keep the bow at right angles to the string.
5. Raise your wrist slightly at the frog and lower it as you draw closer to the tip.
6. Relax your right shoulder, elbow and wrist.

BOW GRIP EXERCISES

Your teacher will explain how to do these exercises.

1. Pinkie Lifter
2. Flex
3. Wave
4. Teeter-Totter
5. Squeeze-Relax
6. Windshield Wiper
7. Spider
8. Rocket Launch

Cello

INSTRUMENT POSITION

1. Sit with the correct posture.
   See figure 6.

2. Adjust the end pin so that the lowest tuning peg is even with your left ear.

3. Place the end pin in a rock stop or cello board.

4. Be sure that:
   a. the cello rests lightly against your chest.
   b. your shoulders are relaxed and square.
   c. both feet are flat on the floor with the left foot slightly forward.
   d. both knees are lightly balancing the instrument.
   e. the cello is turned slightly to the right.
   See figure 6.

5. Relax both shoulders.

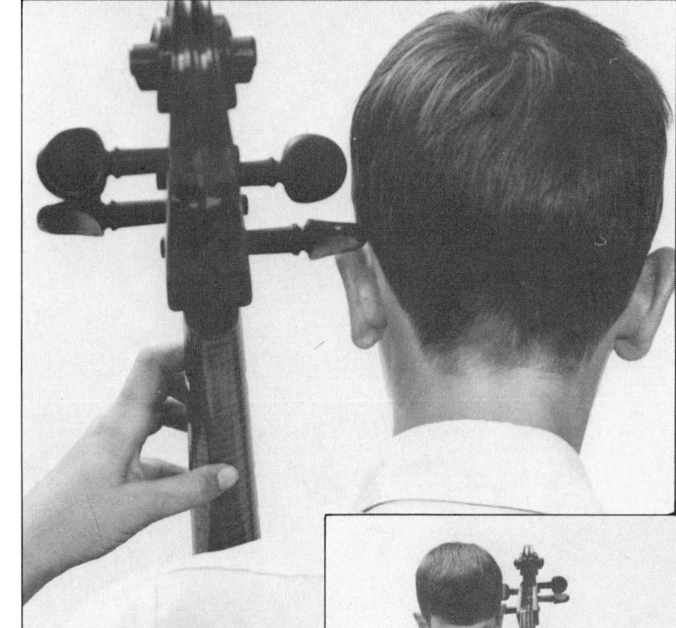

Figure 5

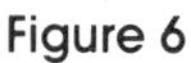

Figure 6

LEFT HAND POSITION

1. Place the pad of the thumb on the center of the neck behind the middle finger.
   See figure 5.

2. Curve your fingers over the fingerboard. They should cross the strings almost at right angles.
   See figure 7.

3. Adjust your wrist and forearm to form a straight line.

4. Be sure that:
   a. your thumb is relaxed.
   b. your thumb and first finger form a letter "C".
   c. your thumb and second finger are opposite each other.
   d. your elbow does not rest on the instrument.
   e. your fingernails are cut short.

5. Relax your left shoulder.
   See figures 5 and 7.

Figure 7

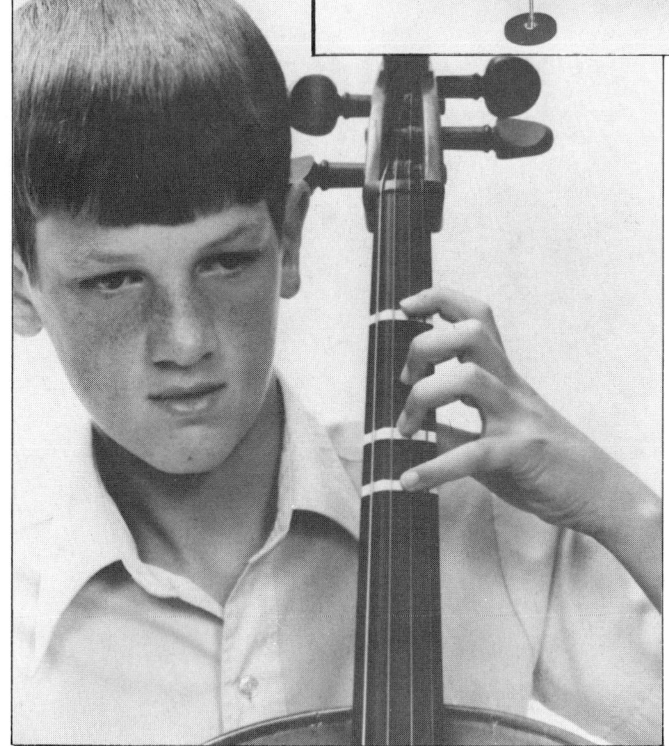

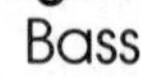

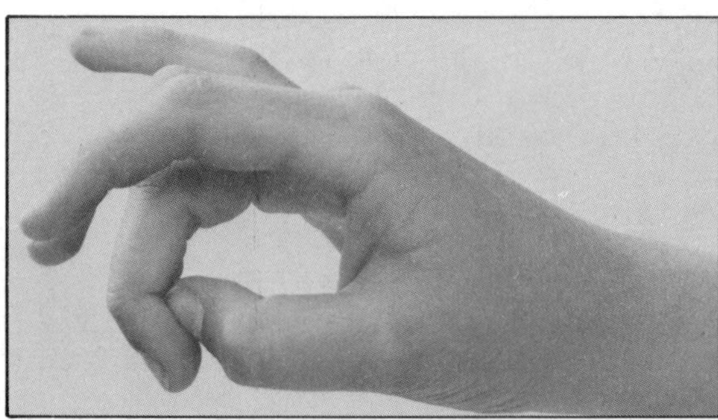

Figure 1

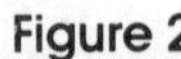

Figure 2

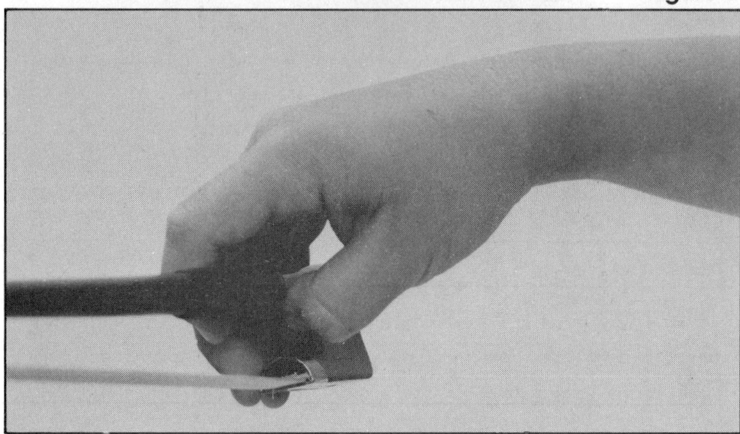

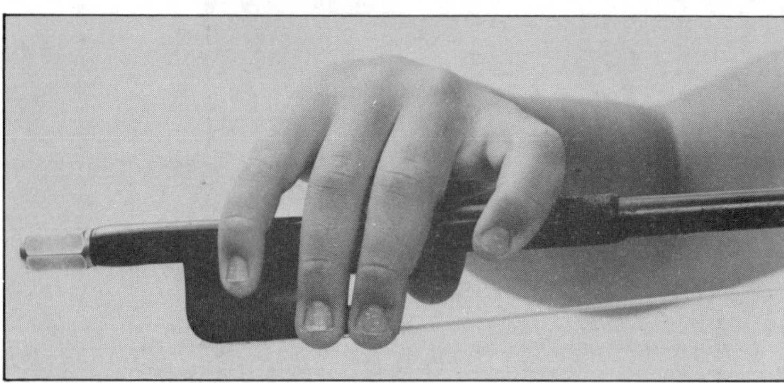

Figure 3

Figure 4

BOW GRIP FRENCH BOW

1. Make a **circle** with the tip of your thumb on the first joint or crease of your middle finger. **Keep your thumb bent.**
   See figure 1.
2. a. Holding the middle of your bow (pencil) with your left hand, lift your right hand thumb and place the stick (pencil) on the first joint or crease of your middle finger.
   b. Place the tip of the thumb on the stick (pencil) next to the frog.
   Keep your circle.
   Keep your thumb bent.
   See figure 2.
3. a. Turn your hand inward or toward the tip of the bow.
   b. Place your index finger at the first joint over the stick (pencil).
   See figure 3.
4. Lay your ring finger comfortably over the stick (pencil) on the frog.
   See figure 3.
5. Place your little finger at the first joint over the stick (pencil).
   See figure 3.
6. Check your entire bow grip.
   Reminder: THUMB BENT
   FINGERS CURVED OVER THE STICK
   HAND RELAXED
   See figures 2 and 3.

BOWING

1. Place the bow on the string half way between the bridge and the fingerboard.
   See figures 4 and 7.
2. Tilt the bow stick slightly toward the fingerboard (away from the bridge).
   See figures 4 and 7.
3. Press the bow firmly into the string.
4. Move the bow in a straight line with the bridge. Keep the bow at right angles to the string.
5. Raise your wrist slightly at the frog and lower it as you draw closer to the tip.
6. Relax your right shoulder, elbow and wrist.

BOW GRIP EXERCISES

Your teacher will explain how to do these exercises.

1. Pinkie Lifter
2. Flex
3. Wave
4. Teeter-Totter
5. Squeeze-Relax
6. Windshield Wiper
7. Spider
8. Rocket Launch

Bass

BOW GRIP GERMAN BOW

1. Holding the middle of your bow with your left hand, place the adjusting screw in the web of your right hand.
   See figure 5.
2. Place your thumb, slightly curved, on top of the stick.
   See figure 6.
3. Rest your first and second fingers along the side of the stick. Keep them slightly curved.
4. Bend your third finger and rest it in the curve of the frog.
5. Place your little finger under the frog close to the hair.
   See figure 6.
6. Check your entire bow grip.
   Reminder: FINGERS CURVED
   BOW HELD BY THE FINGER TIPS
   NOT IN THE PALM
   HAND RELAXED
   See figure 6.

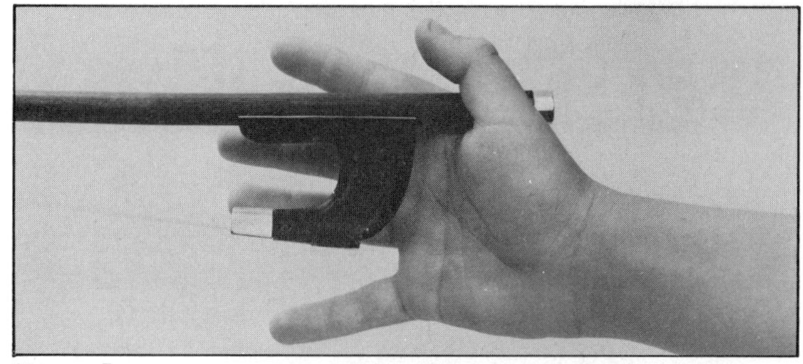

Figure 5

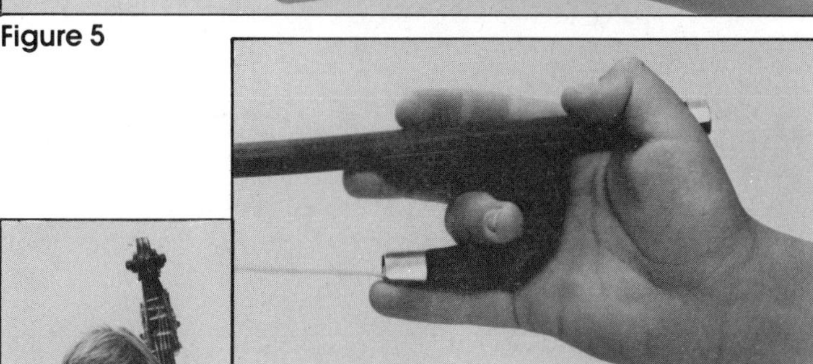

Figure 6

INSTRUMENT POSITION

1. Stand with the correct posture.
   See figures 4 and 7.
2. Adjust the end pin so that the lowest tuning peg is even with your left ear.
3. Place the end pin in a rock stop or bass board.
4. Be sure that:
   a. both feet are separated with the left foot forward and to the left.
   b. the bass is inclined towards you.
   c. the upper bout is resting against the left groin area.
   d. the inside left knee is resting lightly against the back of the bass.
   e. you lean into the bass.
   See figures 4 and 7.
5. Relax both shoulders.

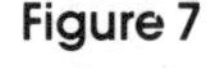

Figure 7

LEFT HAND POSITION

1. Place the pad of the thumb on the center of the neck behind the middle finger.
   See figure 8.
2. Curve your fingers over the fingerboard with the first finger pointing upward.
   See figure 9.
3. Adjust your wrist and forearm to form a straight line.
   See figures 8 and 9.
4. Be sure that:
   a. your thumb is relaxed.
   b. equal distance exists between 1st and 2nd fingers and the 2nd and 4th fingers.
   c. your thumb and second finger are opposite each other.
   d. your elbow does not rest on the instrument.
   e. your fingernails are cut short.
5. Relax your left shoulder.

Figure 8

Figure 9

BOW GRIP EXERCISES

TEACHER:
The purpose of these bow grip exercises is to strengthen the muscles that hold the bow. The right hand must be relaxed and flexible to produce a full rounded tone as well as to execute complex bowings and string crossings. It is through strength that the hand is able to be relaxed and flexible. Have your students practice these exercises to develop the necessary strength.

Do an exercise or two as part of each lesson. Encourage your students to do several each day during home practice. It is through everyday practice that a student will most quickly strengthen his/her hand and arm.

Caution all students to be careful and not to drop the bow or hit the bow on anything as they do these exercises. Bows are very fragile and great care must always be exercised in handling the bow.

The instructions below are written so that you, the teacher, can read them as the students execute each step of each exercise.

Pinkie Lifter

1. Hold the middle of your bow with your left hand, the frog to the right.
2. Position it in front of you and parallel to the floor.
3. Place the right hand on the bow using the proper bow grip.
4. Lift your little finger (pinkie) up off the stick. Violinists and violists should keep the little finger curved.
5. Place your little finger (curved) back on the stick in a good bow grip position.
6. Repeat many times. Relax when your hand gets tired.

Flex

1. Hold the middle of your bow with your left hand, the frog to the right.
2. Place the right hand on the bow using the proper bow grip.
3. Keeping all your fingers on the bow, slowly straighten your right hand fingers as much as possible.
4. Keeping all your fingers on the bow, slowly curve your right hand fingers as much as possible.
5. The motion is much like opening and closing your fist (without the bow).
6. Repeat many times. Relax when your hand gets tired.

Wave

1. Hold the middle of your bow with your left hand, the frog to the right.
2. Place the right hand on the bow using the proper bow grip.
3. Hold both arms straight out in front of you.
4. Wave bye-bye with your right hand. Bend the wrist and keep a good bow grip.
5. Repeat many times. Relax when your hand gets tired.

Teeter-Totter

1. Place the right hand on the bow using the proper bow grip.
2. Hold the bow out in front of you parallel to the floor.
3. Slowly straighten your little finger by pushing downward. The tip of the bow should go up.
4. Slowly relax your little finger allowing it to curve. The tip of the bow should go down.
5. Your bow should go up and down like a teeter-totter as you repeat straightening and curving your little finger. Your thumb will be the fulcrum of the teeter-totter. Do not turn your wrist to make the bow move. Use your little finger.
6. Repeat this many times. Relax when your hand gets tired.
7. This exercise can also be done at the balance point toward the middle of the bow.

Squeeze–Relax

1. Hold the middle of your bow with your left hand, the frog to the right.
2. Place the right hand on the bow using the proper bow grip.
3. Hold both arms straight out in front of you.
4. Squeeze your fingers tightly, then relax. It is in this relaxed position that you should hold your bow when playing.

Windshield Wiper

1. Place the right hand on the bow using the proper bow grip.
2. Hold your bow straight out in front of you. Point your bow straight up.
3. Make your bow go back and forth like a windshield wiper. Keep a good bow grip.
4. Repeat many times. Relax when your hand gets tired.
5. This exercise can also be done with wide, slow movements or narrow, fast movements.

Spider

1. Place the right hand on the bow using the proper bow grip.
2. Hold your bow straight out in front of you. Point your bow straight up.
3. Keeping a good bow grip, crawl with your fingers to the tip of the bow. When you get to the tip, crawl back to the frog. Be sure to keep your thumb bent and your little finger curved.
4. Repeat many times. Relax when your hand gets tired.

Rocket Launch

1. Place the right hand on the bow using the proper bow grip.
2. Hold your bow straight out in front of you. Point the bow straight up.
3. Keeping your bow straight up and down, raise the bow as high as you can.
4. Keeping your bow straight up and down, lower the bow as low as you can.
5. Be sure your wrist is as flexible when you play your instrument as when you practice the Rocket Launch.
6. Repeat many times. Relax when your hand gets tired.
7. This exercise can be done either slow or fast.

COLOR CODED SYMBOLS

Each of the following items is highlighted by a color-coded symbol:

NEW NOTES are identified by the BLUE symbol. 

NEW IDEAS are identified by the RED symbol. 

THEORY GAMES are identified by the GRAY symbol. 

In the score, all of these symbols appear in ONE COLOR.

THEORY GAMES

The Theory Games provide an opportunity for the student to demonstrate his/her knowledge and understanding of the concepts being taught. Also, young students generally need extra reinforcement of naming notes and counting rhythms. These areas should be checked frequently by either naming the notes orally or by written assignment.

MARGINS

The margins provide an excellent space to have students record the date of assignments, grades by the teacher, stickers for graded performance, special notes and comments, or check marks indicating the completion of the line.

STARTING BY ROTE

There are many advantages to starting string students by a rote process or system. The biggest advantage is that the students can concentrate on playing positions and bowing habits without the added problem of reading music.

The STARTING BY ROTE section presents a unique and flexible way to start string students with a minimum amount of reading material. This section utilizes the notes of the D Major Scale with several songs added for musical interest. The use of this rote section is highly recommended before starting music reading to establish good playing positions and bowing habits.

The letters printed in this rote section are the names of the notes the students should play. The student should be assigned one of the rhythm patterns and play that pattern ONCE for each letter. For technique development and variety, several rhythm patterns are listed throughout this rote section. However, any rhythm pattern(s) may be used with this entire rote section thereby making this rote section completely flexible according to each teacher's favorite starting rhythms. Additionally, there are blanks under each Rhythm Pattern to allow the student or teacher to use other words for each rhythm. Perhaps the name of a school, the name of a town or the name of a student would add interest to a particular pattern. Any pattern can be used. Be creative!

The songs in this rote section are presented in a slightly different format. The letters printed are the notes of the song with each letter representing one note value. The music is printed in the score for the teacher's reference. The teacher is encouraged to play each song for the student. This may be done on a stringed instrument, piano or any other instrument. The students can then use the letter names for reference in their home practice of these songs.

Each line should be memorized as quickly as possible so that complete attention can be given to establishing good playing positions and bowing habits. Of course listening should be emphasized. Good tone and accurate intonation should always be the primary goals of each line and exercise. However, making a good tone and playing with accurate intonation is only possible with good playing positions and bowing habits.

Go slowly to establish good playing positions and bowing habits. If by the end of the rote section the students are playing with good playing positions, the next section of the book STARTING BY NOTE should follow quite smoothly.

COUNTING SYSTEM FOR RHYTHMS

Throughout this book the traditional system of counting rhythms is presented in the Rhythm Boxes. However, if the teacher wishes to teach another system of counting it may be written in the Rhythm Boxes at the space provided for Alternate Counting.

It makes no difference what system of counting is used to teach the reading of rhythms to beginners but that a system MUST indeed be taught. It is suggested that whatever system is chosen that it be used as follows:

Clapping and Counting Rhythms

1. Clap once for each note. Hands should remain together for the duration of each note.
2. Count aloud.
3. Count (but do not clap) the rests. Part hands for rests.
4. In the case of tied notes clap only the first note.

Playing and Counting Rhythms

1. Play arco or pizzicato on any one pitch.
2. Count aloud.
3. Count (but do not play) the rests.

It must be emphasized that both CLAPPING the rhythms **and** COUNTING ALOUD are the keys to students learning a counting system. One without the other does not seem to be nearly as successful.

Virtually every line or exercise in this book is a rhythm exercise. Each line or exercise should be clapped and counted. Also, each line can be played on any one pitch using the rhythm of the written notes.

Students will develop into excellent readers of rhythms if the techniques outlined above are followed.

SEPARATING RIGHT HAND AND LEFT HAND

Because the technique of playing a stringed instrument is so complex with each hand doing a completely different motion from the other, it is very beneficial to practice an exercise or song concentrating only on one hand. By isolating one hand, the student can focus on the techniques of that particular hand. Below are several ideas which may be applied to many exercises or songs.

Right Hand

1. Play the rhythms of the exercise or song all the way through on one pitch. This pitch could be an open string or a fingered note. This will allow the student to concentrate on any of the following right hand technique items:
   a. tone
   b. rhythm
   c. bow division/bowing
   d. bow arm
2. Play the exercise or song all the way through using only open strings, i.e. any note that is played on the D string will be played open D and any note that is played on the A string will be played open A. If other strings are included in the exercise or song, they too can be incorporated into this practice technique. The student can concentrate on one of the following technique items:
   a. string crossings
   b. tone
   c. bow division/bowing
   d. bow arm
   e. rhythm

Left Hand

1. Play the exercise or song all the way through playing pizzicato. The student can concentrate on the following:
   a. intonation
   b. left hand position
   c. rhythm
2. Slowly play the exercise or song all the way through using only one note value regardless of what is written, i.e. play a quarter note for each note rather than the rhythm written. This is most effective when played slowly and using a long note value. Practicing in this fashion will improve the following:
   a. intonation
   b. tone
   c. difficult fingering combination

PRACTICE

Regular practice is necessary in learning to play a musical instrument. Encourage your students to practice in several short sessions each day rather than one long session. Playing a stringed instrument requires strength with flexibility. Long practice sessions cause the muscles to tire and become tight and rigid making flexibility almost impossible. As the students become stronger, their practice sessions can be lengthened. This principle should also be applied to lessons, classes and rehearsals. The practice record below may be copied and attached to each student's book.

You, as teacher, should assist young students in establishing goals for each lesson, practice session and assignment. Students will make better progress if they work for specific goals rather than just "putting in" their prescribed minutes of practice. These goals, in addition to the correct notes, should include:

- correct bow grip
- correct instrument position
- good tone quality
- good intonation
- correct rhythm
- correct bowing and bow division
- better bow control
- steady tempo
- good musical phrasing

PRACTICE RECORD

WEEK	Sun.	Mon.	Tues.	Wed.	Thurs.	Fri.	Sat.	Total Time	Parents Initials
1									
2									
3									
4									
5									
6									
7									
8									
9									
10									
11									
12									
13									
14									
15									
16									
17									
18									
19									
20									

TEACHER: Feel free to duplicate copies of the certificate below and present to your students upon completion of ALL FOR STRINGS–Book 1.

This is to certify that

____

has successfully completed

Book 1

of

All for STRINGS

Comprehensive String Method

_______________ _______________________

Date Teacher's Signature

STARTING BY ROTE

THE BASICS

DOWN BOW	UP BOW	PIZZICATO
⊓	V	*pizz.*
Move the bow toward the tip.	Move the bow toward the frog.	Pluck the string with the index finger of your right hand.

INSTRUCTIONS

RHYTHM PATTERN

Play the assigned Rhythm Pattern ONCE for each letter using pizzicato or arco.

PIZZICATO (Violin and Viola)

1. Place your index finger (1st finger) on the correct string.
2. Place your thumb on the corner of the fingerboard.
3. Pull the string firmly to the side to produce a good ringing tone.
4. Check your right hand pizzicato position.

ARCO

1. Place your bow at the correct string level.
2. Play in the middle of the bow.
3. Use a forearm stroke to PULL the bow.
4. Check your right hand bow grip often.
5. Play with a good ringing tone.

TEACHER: Point out to students that they should read the Fingering Charts as if their instrument were facing them. The String Level Charts should be read as if they were looking down the strings at the bridge with the instrument in playing position.

TEACHER: Have all students constantly check the pictures on student book pages 4 and 5 to establish a good instrument position and bow grip. Establishing good habits now will make them better players.

NEW NOTES

Violin

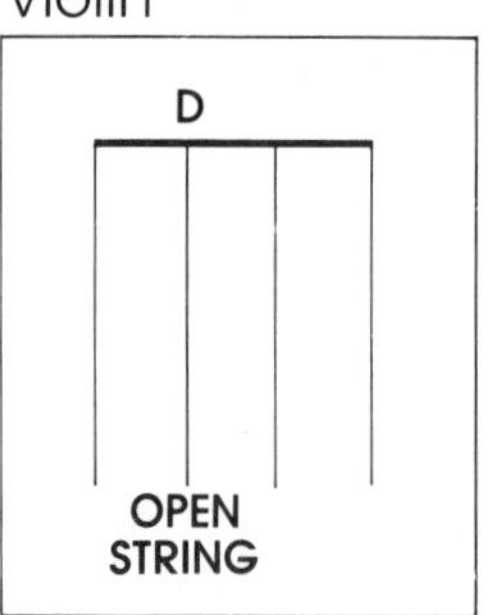

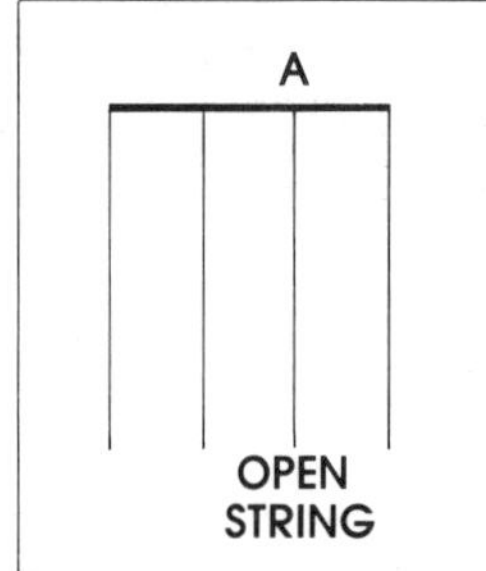

Viola

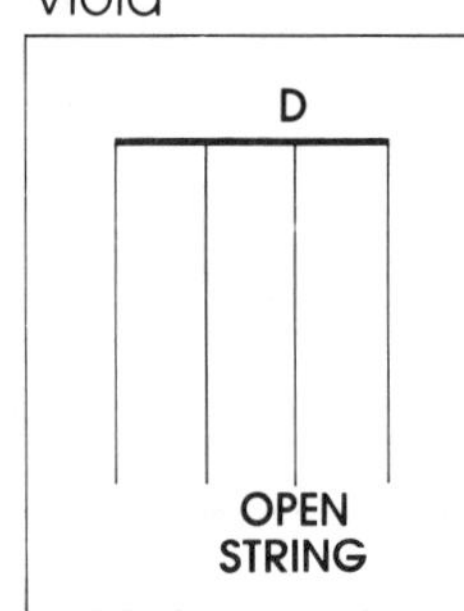

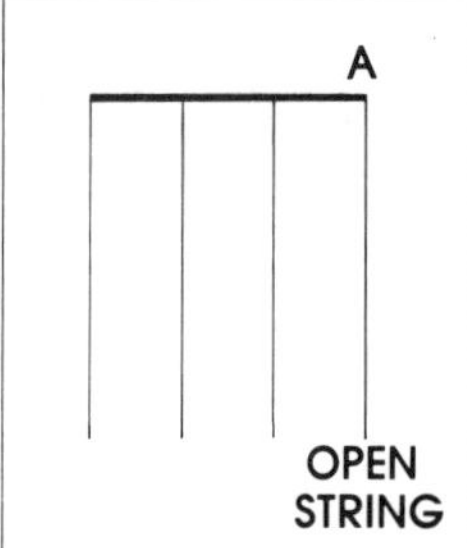

Cello

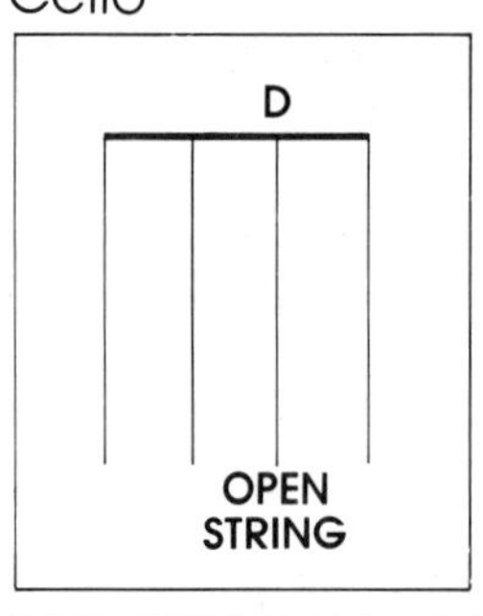

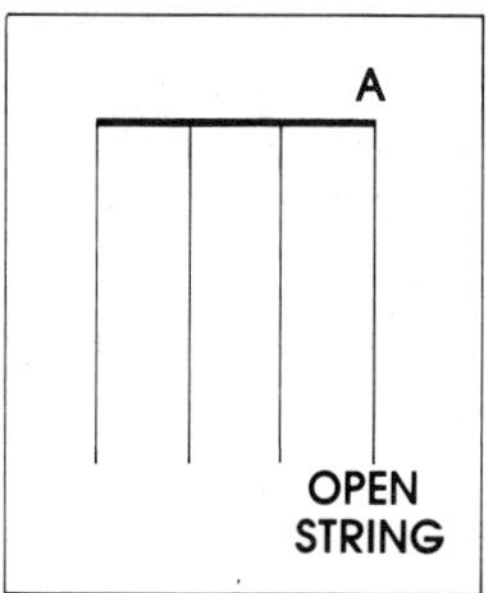

Bass

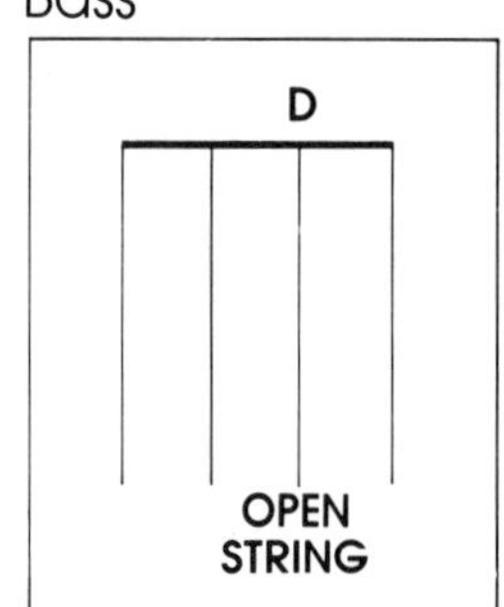

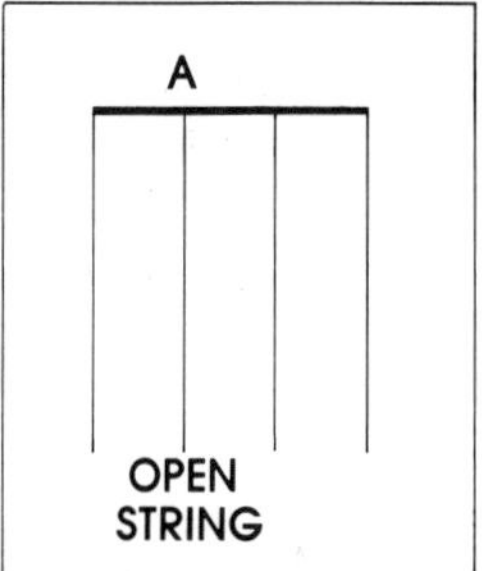

Violin

STRING LEVEL

Adjust your arm to play on the correct string.

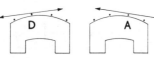

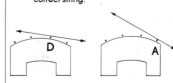

D A

Viola

STRING LEVEL

Adjust your arm to play on the correct string.

D A

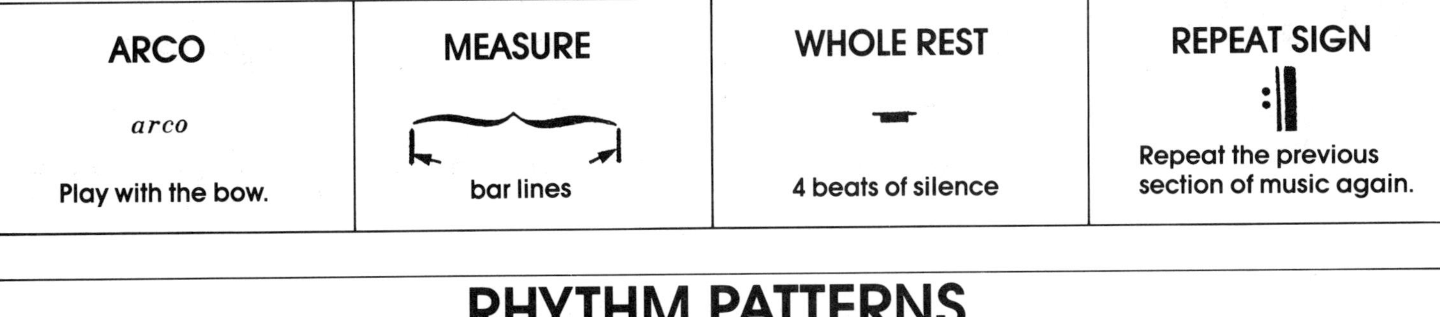

ARCO
arco
Play with the bow.
MEASURE
bar lines
WHOLE REST
4 beats of silence
REPEAT SIGN
Repeat the previous section of music again.

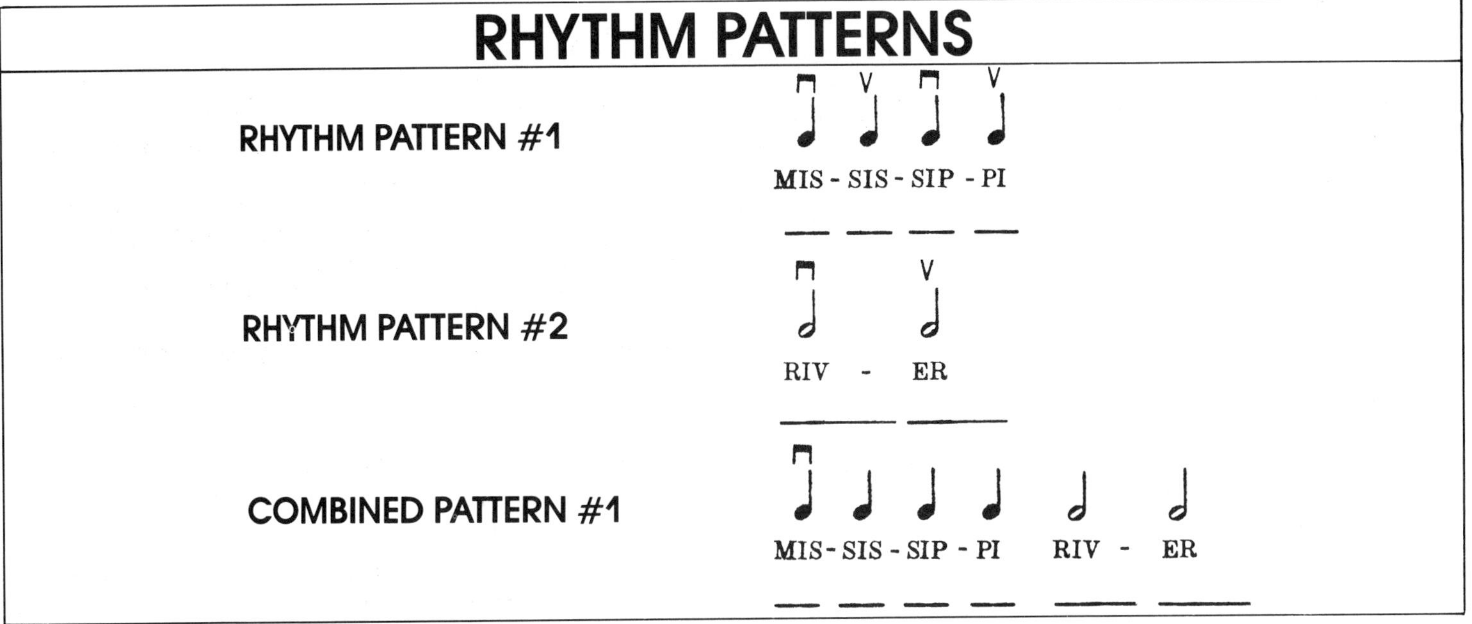

Cello

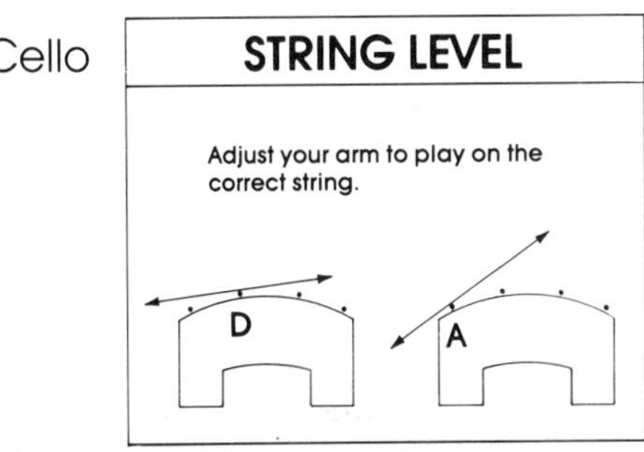

Bass

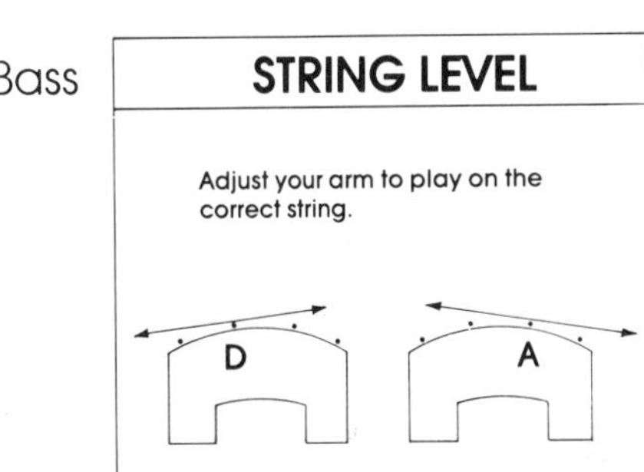

TEACHER: The arm of the string player should be at a different level when playing on each string because the plane for the bow stroke is different for each string. Demonstrate on a stringed instrument and draw diagrams on the chalkboard to make certain the students understand these important points of string playing.

TEACHER: Check the playing positions of your string players often. Have the students check each other to make them aware of the important points of holding the bow, holding the instrument, posture and bowing.

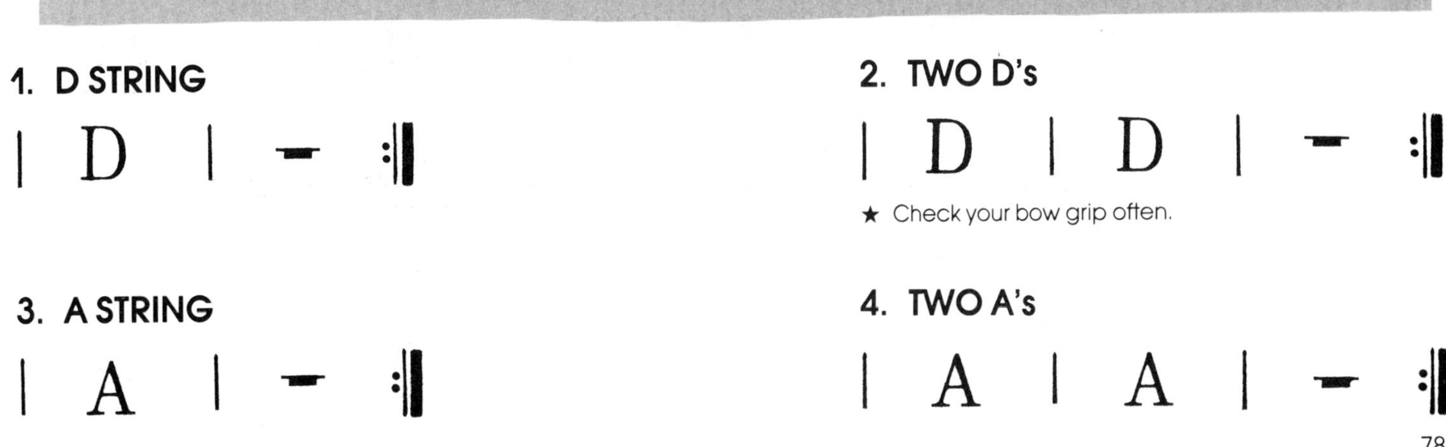

TEACHER: Have all students make good crisp bow preparations so that they are ready to play on the new string as soon as possible. Continue these bow preparations throughout the beginning stages, both in the LEARNING BY ROTE and LEARNING BY NOTE sections. It may be helpful to actually stop at each place in the music that requires a bow preparation (string crossing) and have students execute a well-planned, crisp bow change to the new string level. Emphasize playing on the correct string level with these preparations.

NEW IDEA

PREPARE BOW	*	Go to the new string level. Be ready to play on the new string as soon as possible.

5. D AND A

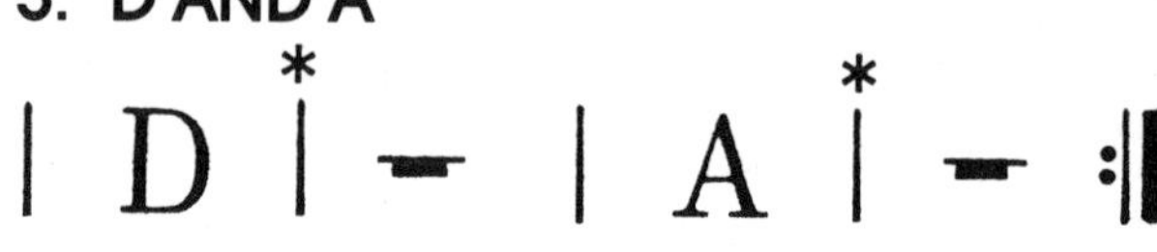

6. FAST PREPARATIONS

NEW NOTE

Violin

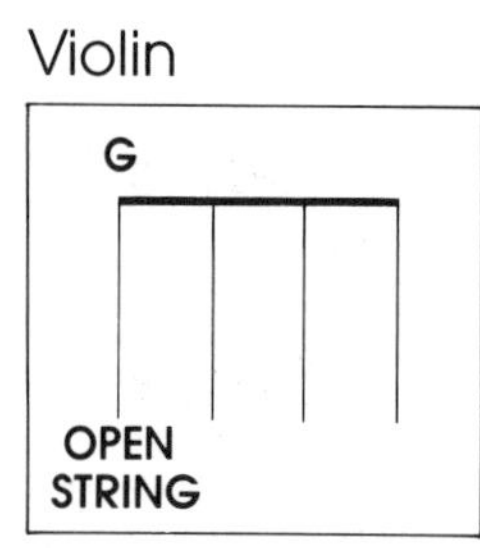

Viola

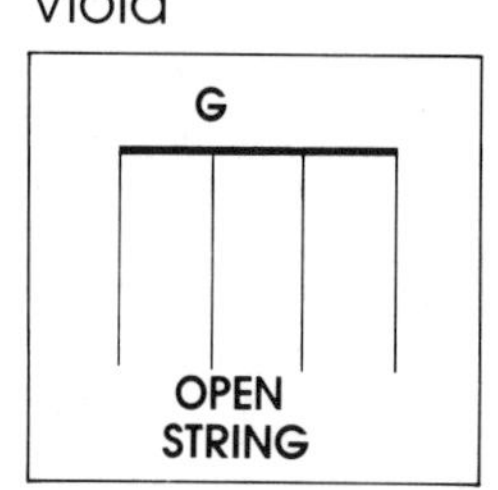

Cello

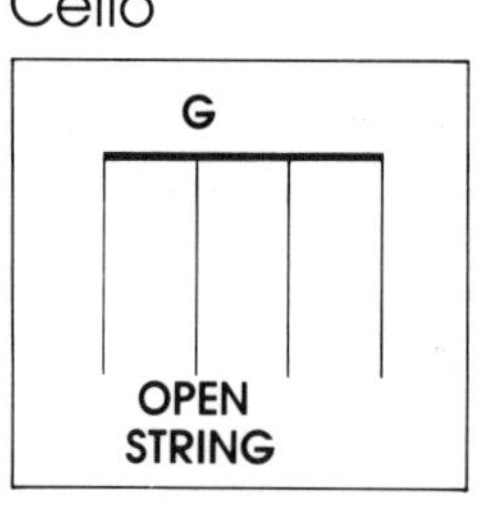

Bass

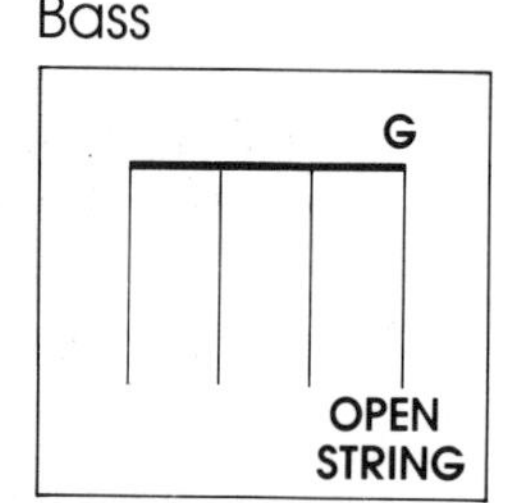

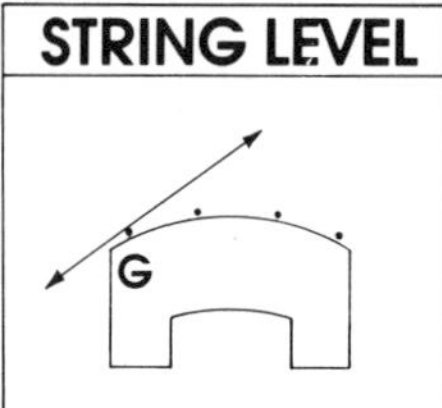

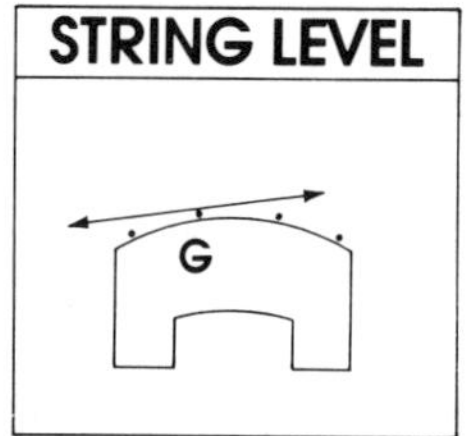

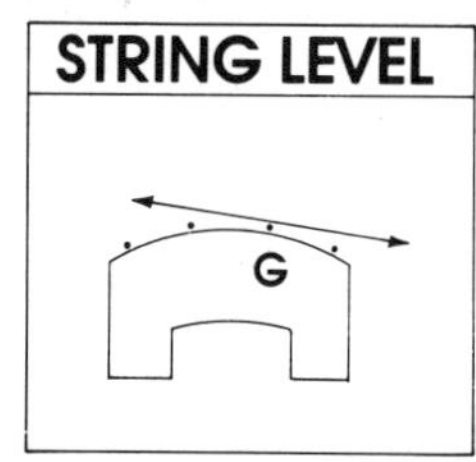

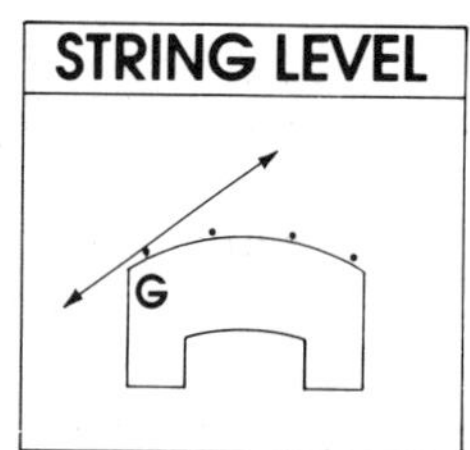

7. G STRING

| G | — :||

8. TWO G'S

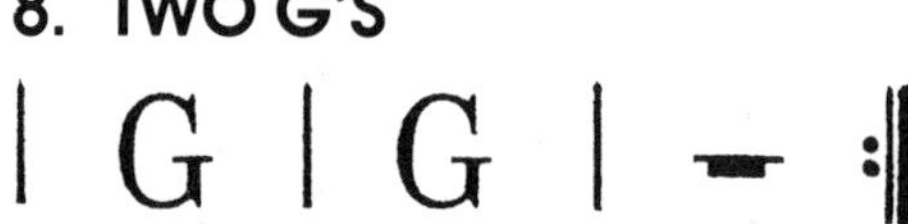

★ Check your bow grip often.

9. G AND D

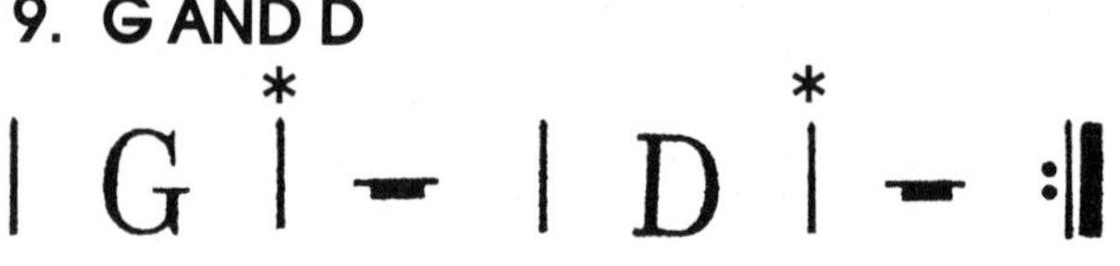

★ Is your right thumb bent?

10. FAST PREPARATIONS

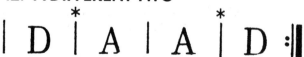

★ Roll the bow to a new string.

11. TWO TOGETHER

| G * | D | D * | G :||

12. A DIFFERENT TWO

| D * | A | A * | D :||

13. THREE STRINGS

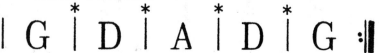

| G * | D * | A * | D * | G :||

★ Be sure to use fast bow preparations.

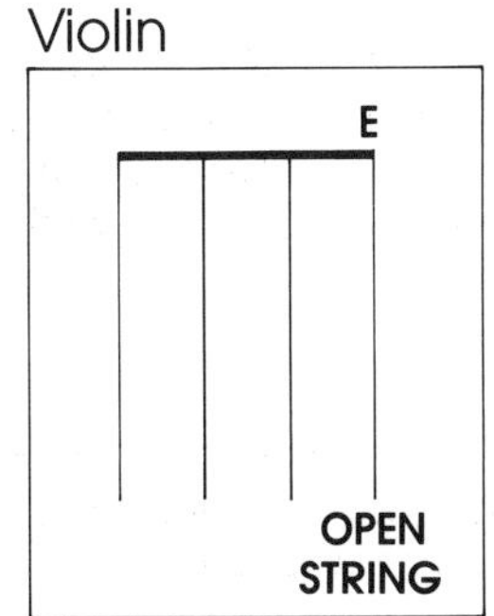

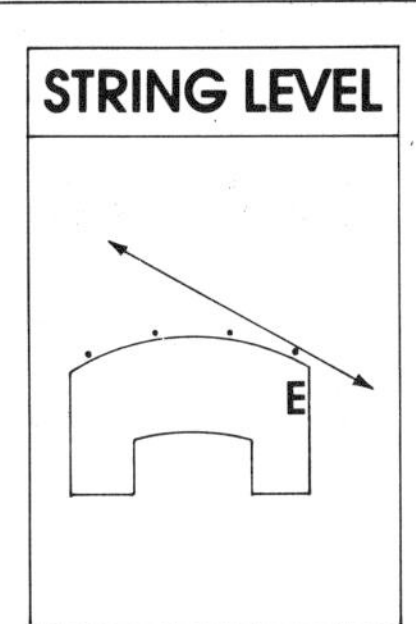

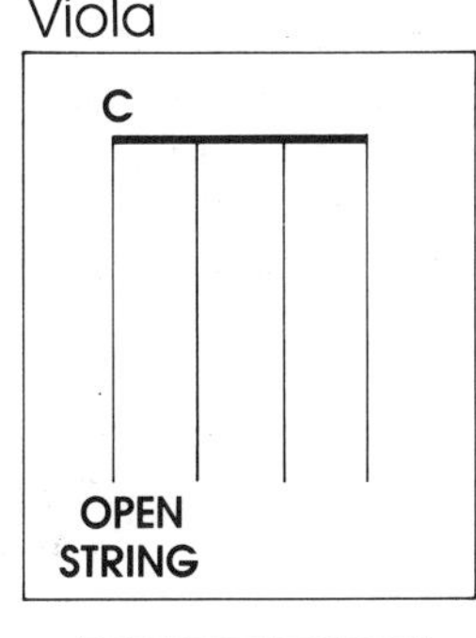

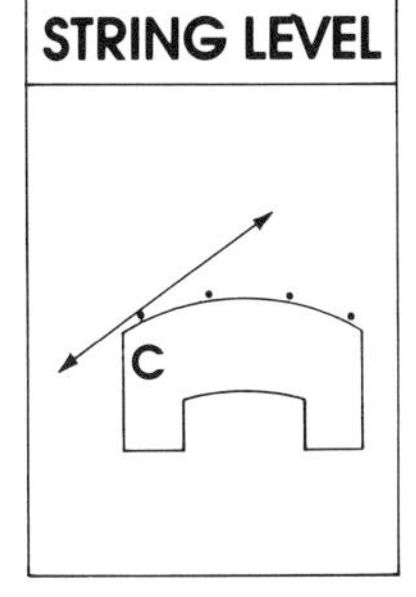

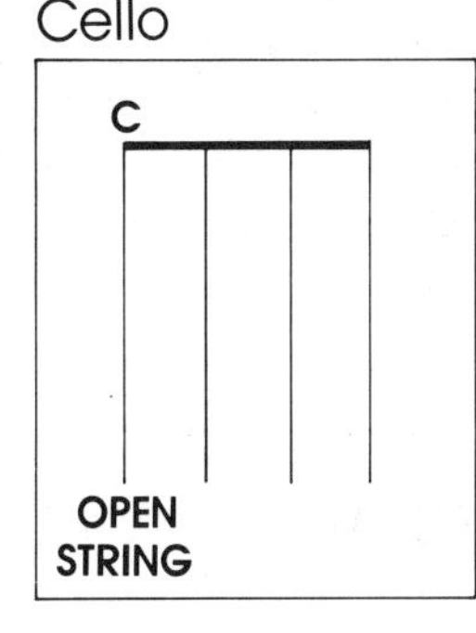

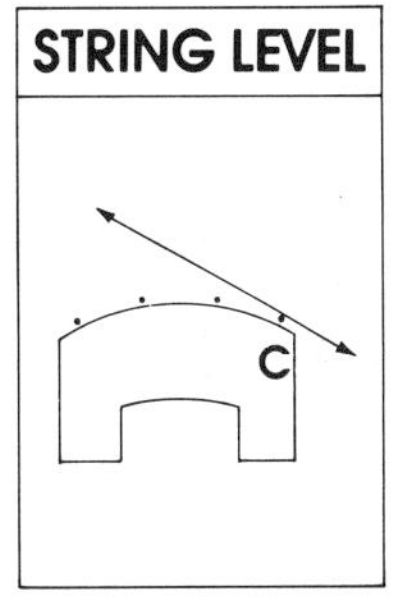

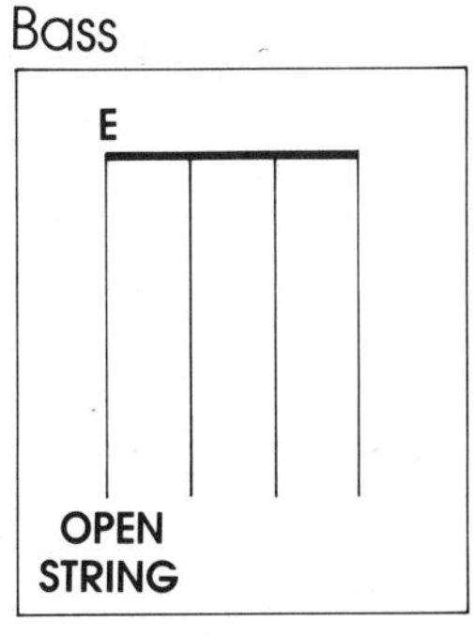

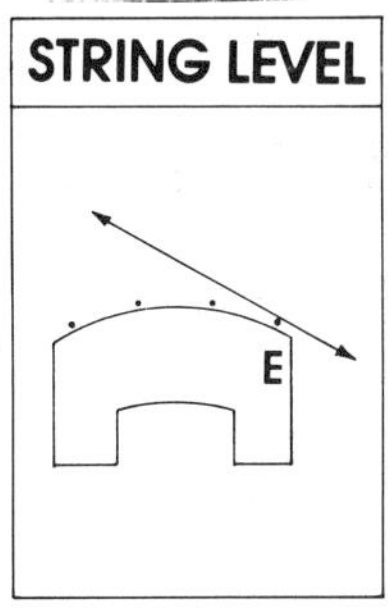

TEACHER: Both open E strings (violin, bass) and open C strings (viola, cello) are introduced at the same time in line 14. Alert the students that they will be playing in harmony on lines 14, 15 and part of 18.

14. E OR C STRING

15. TWO TOGETHER

Violin Bass | E | E | – :||

Viola Cello | C | C | – :||

TEACHER: The rests at the beginning or end of this line make it possible to play the line in unison as well as to allow time for the bows to cross over all four strings to prepare for the repeat.

16. ALL FOUR STRINGS

★ Roll the bow to the new string.

17. A BIG JUMP

| G * | – | A * | – :||

★ Check your bow grip often.

18. BIG PREPARATIONS

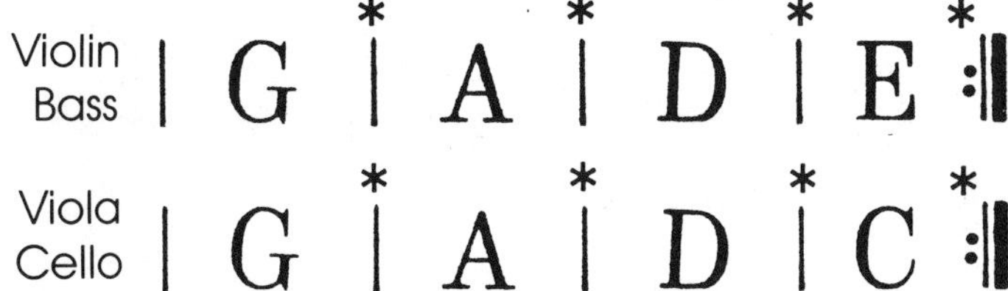

TEACHER: The CIRCLE OF STRINGS is a wonderful line to use for warm up and study/review of bowings. Have students memorize this line so that they can use it with all bowings and rhythms introduced throughout this book.

19. CIRCLE OF STRINGS

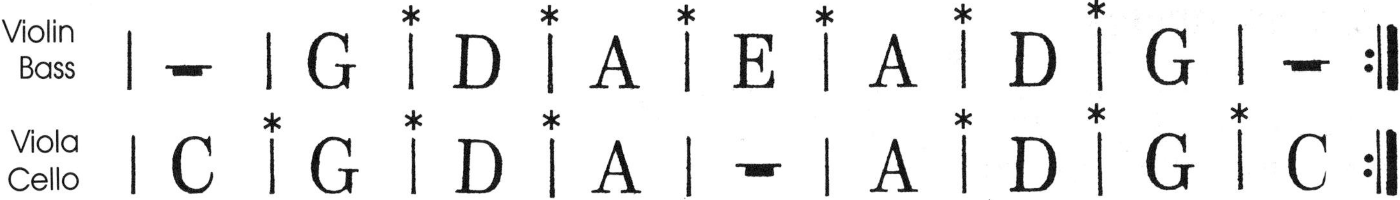

★ Be sure to use fast bow preparations.

MORE RHYTHM PATTERNS

RHYTHM PATTERN #3	ROS - IN
RHYTHM PATTERN #4	BOW
COMBINED PATTERN #2	ROS - IN BOW
COMBINED PATTERN #3	BOW ROS - IN

INSTRUCTIONS

Play all the preceding lines with these new rhythm patterns.

STUDENT BOOK—Page 9

NEW NOTE

Violin

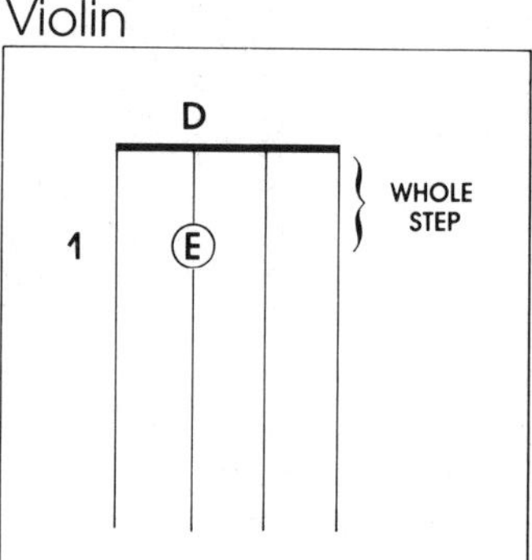

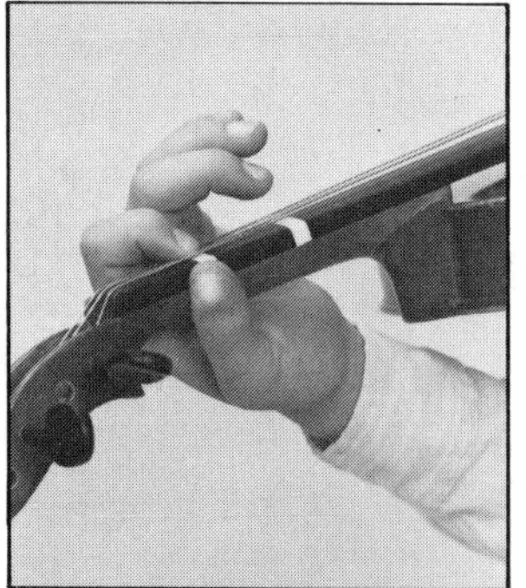

Viola

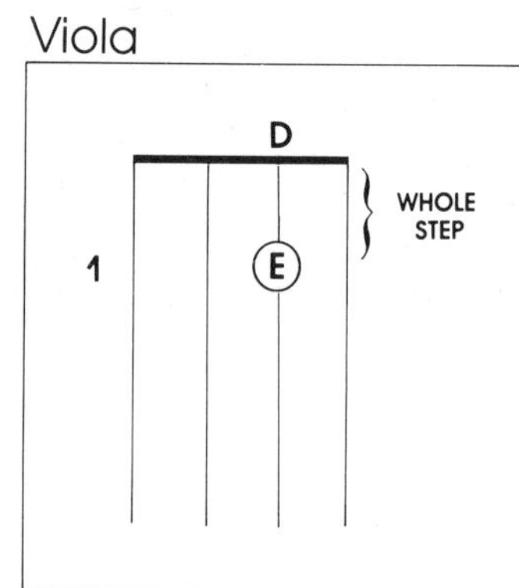

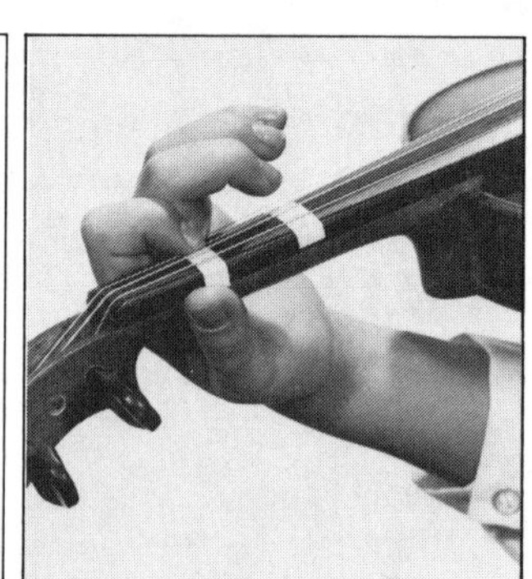

Cello

D
1
E
WHOLE STEP

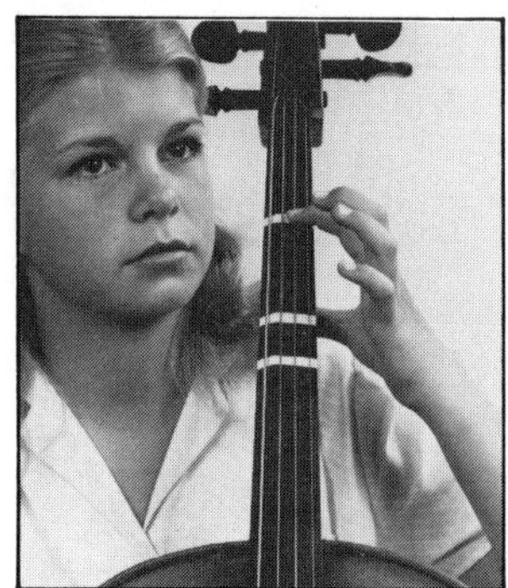

Bass

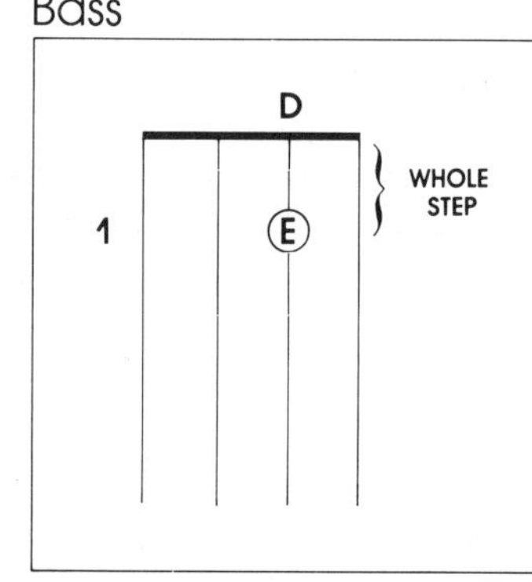

20. NEW NOTE E

| E | – :||

★ Place your first finger on the D string.

21. UP TO E

| D | – | E | – :||

★ Prepare your first finger during the rest.

22. PLAY TWO

| D | E | – :||

★ Check the placement of your bow.

23. NO RESTS

| D | E | E | D :||

TEACHER: Some students may need additional help to feel the proper bow speed for each of the rhythm patterns. Violin and viola players can do the "Soldier Bowing". This is done by holding the bow with the hair up. The thumb is placed below the frog on the stick and the fingers are placed on top of the frog. The bow is placed on the left shoulder with the stick down. Cello and bass players hold the bow in the same manner. Place the stick of the bow in the palm of the left hand. The left hand should be held in a position that would most closely allow for natural bowing angle. Have students practice the rhythms they are having difficulty with. This is an excellent way to feel the movement of the wrist and to learn rhythms and bowings.

NEW NOTE

Violin

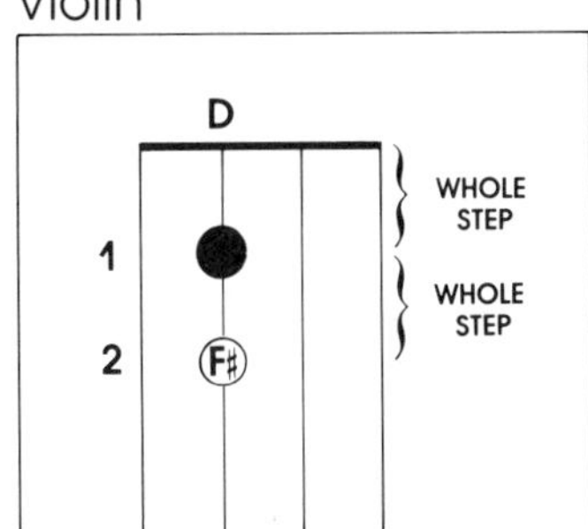

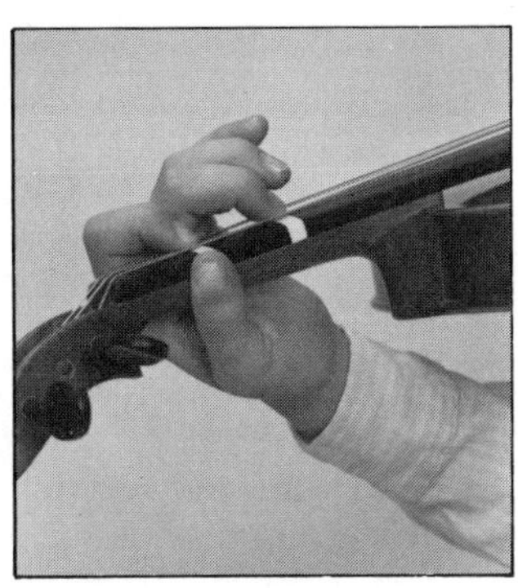

Viola

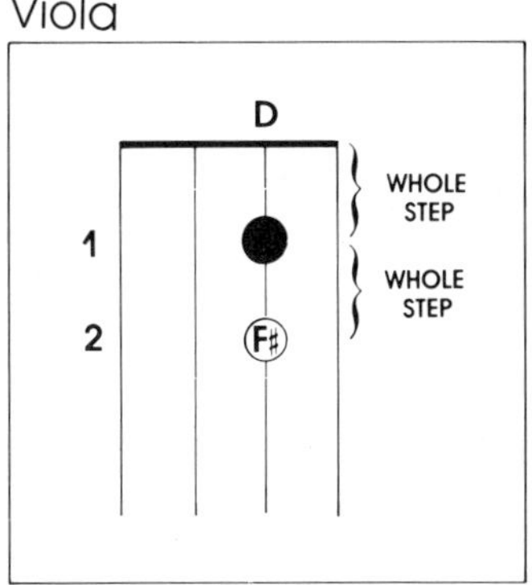

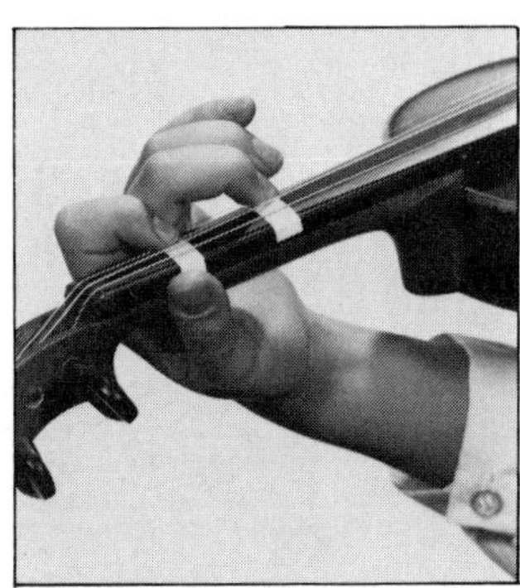

Cello

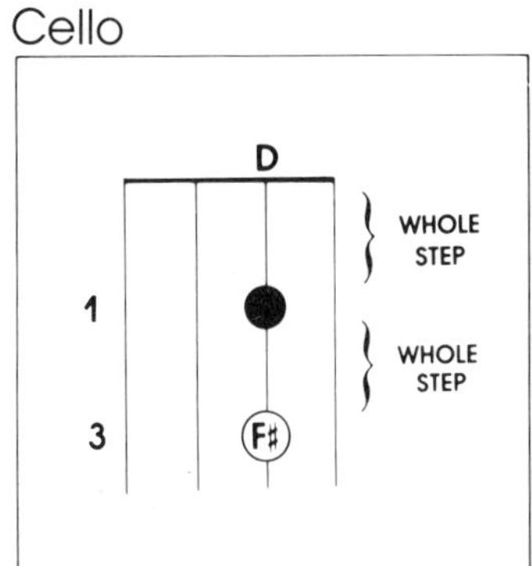

Bass

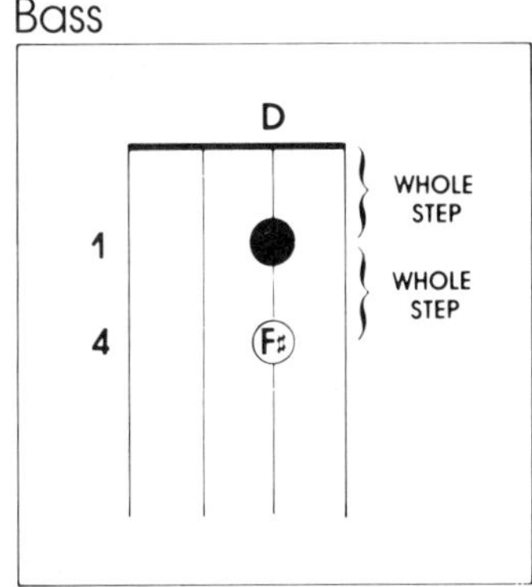

TEACHER: Have students place the finger(s) down before starting the exercise to set the proper hand position, then lift the finger(s). This not only helps develop the proper position of the left hand but also the proper placement of the fingers for good intonation. Use this exercise frequently, especially when new notes are being introduced and when reinforcing finger patterns.

TEACHER: Helping string players to feel the placement of the bow at the frog-middle-tip and top is necessary in order to draw a straight bow. This can be done with an exercise called "Lift and Set". Students should place the bow at the frog with good position and then lift and set the bow at the tip and the middle. Tapping the bow on the string at the tip and the middle also helps the student to feel proper bow placement. This also serves as an excellent remedial exercise to correct crooked bowing.

24. NEW NOTE F♯

| F♯ | — :||

★ Place your first and second finger on the D string.
★ Place your first, second and third finger on the D string.
★ Place your first, second, third and fourth finger on the D string.

25. UP TO F♯

| D | — | E | — | F♯ | — :||

★ Prepare each finger during the rest.

26. PLAY THREE

| D | E | F♯ | — :||

★ Check your bow grip often.

27. STARTING ON F♯

| F♯ | E | D | — :||

★ Prepare your fingers for F♯.

28. NO RESTS

| D | E | F♯ | F♯ | E | D :||

★ Check your left hand position.

INSTRUCTIONS

The songs on this page are to be played in a different way.

1. Play one note for each letter. The letter with a line must be held longer.
2. The rhythm words appear under the letters of the first song. These rhythm words will guide you with the rhythm of the song.
3. The other three songs are familiar. If you do not know the songs your teacher will play them for you.

TEACHER: Lines 29, 30, 31 and 32 are written in a different format. The different style printing indicates a different way to play these lines. Follow the instructions above. Each of these lines are written in music notation with piano accompaniment in the score so the teacher may play each of these songs and accompany the students.

TEACHER: THREE NOTE MARCH is the first time that the double bar has been used without the repeat sign. An explanation may be helpful to the student.

29. THREE NOTE MARCH

| D D D D | E E E —— | F♯ F♯ F♯ F♯ | E E E —— |

Mis - sis - sip - pi Ros - in Bow—— Mis - sis - sip - pi Ros - in Bow——

| D D D D | E E E —— | F♯ F♯ E E | D D D —— ‖

Mis - sis - sip - pi Ros - in Bow—— Ros - in Ros - in Ros - in Bow——

30. FRENCH FOLK SONG
|D D D E |F♯ — E — |D F♯ E E |D — |
★ Is your right thumb bent?
|D D D E |F♯ — E — |D F♯ E E |D — ‖
31. HOT CROSS BUNS
|F♯— E— |D — |F♯— E— |D — |
★ Check your bow grip often.
|D D D D |E E E E |F♯— E— |D — ‖

32. MARY HAD A LITTLE LAMB

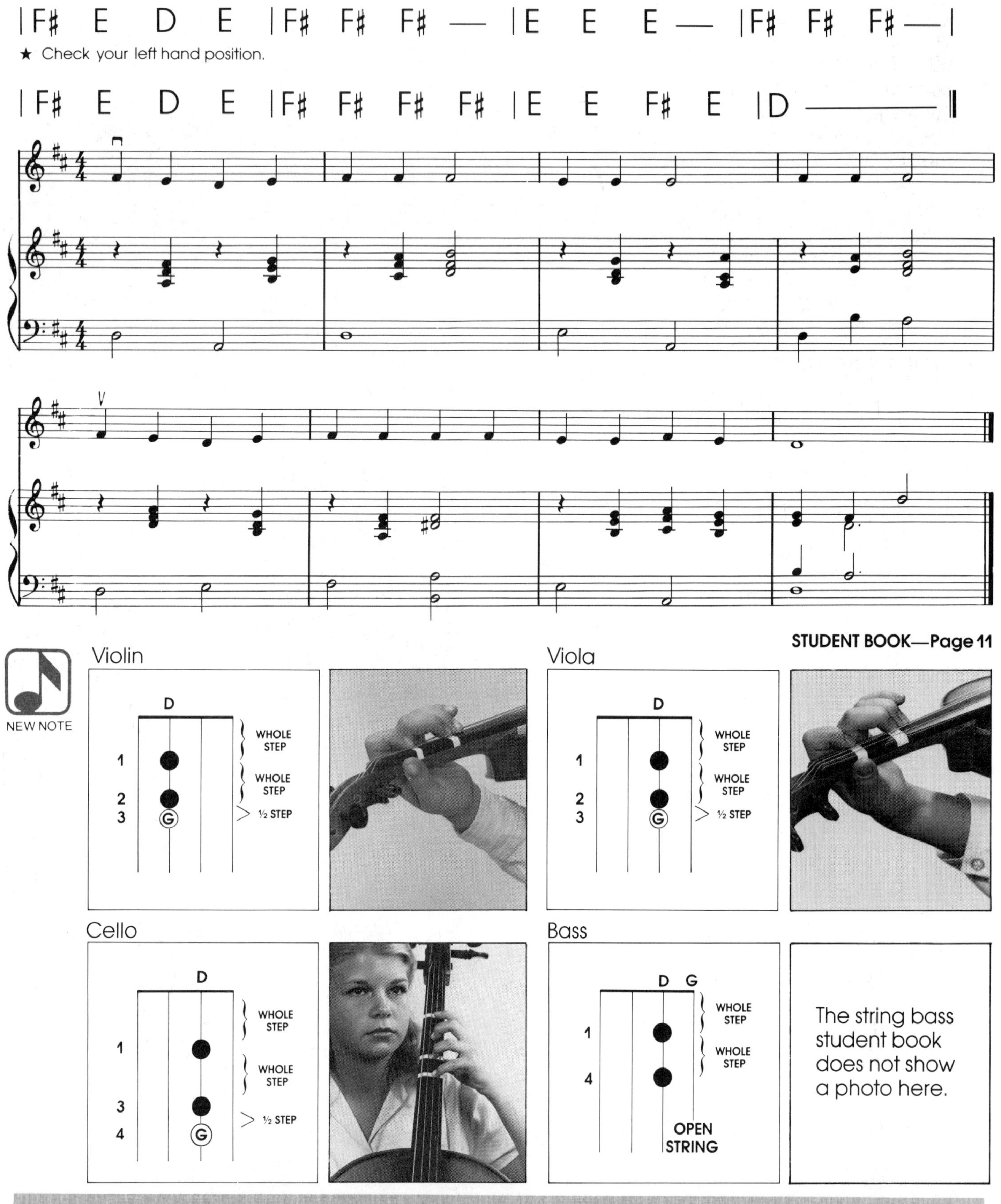

TEACHER: By starting on the new note you can have the students place their fingers down on the string to check for good placement and hand position. Once this is achieved it becomes easier to start on the open string and progress up step-wise to each new note.

33. NEW NOTE G

| G | — :‖

★ Place your first, second and third finger on the D string.

★ Place your first, second, third and fourth finger on the D string.

34. GOING DOWN

| G | F♯ | E | D | — :‖

★ Prepare your fingers for G.

35. MOVIN' UP

| D | E | F♯ | G | G | F♯ | E | D :||

36. ROSIN BOW MARCH

|D D D — |E E E — |F♯ F♯ G G |F♯ F♯ E —|
Ros - in Bow __ Ros - in Bow __ Ros - in Ros - in Ros - in Bow __

|D D D — |E E E — |F♯ F♯ G G |F♯ E D —||

★ Is your right thumb bent?

37. MARCHING SONG

|D D E E |F♯ F♯ G — |F♯ F♯ G G |F♯ F♯ E —|
|D D E E |F♯ F♯ G — |F♯ F♯ G G |F♯ E D —||

★ Check your left hand position.

38. CLIMBING UP

|D E F♯ — |E F♯ G — |F♯ G F♯ E |D E D —‖

★ Check your bow grip often.

STUDENT BOOK—Page 12

TEACHER: Students can practice bowing concepts while they rosin their bows. Make sure that they have the proper hand positions and use full even bow strokes.

Violin

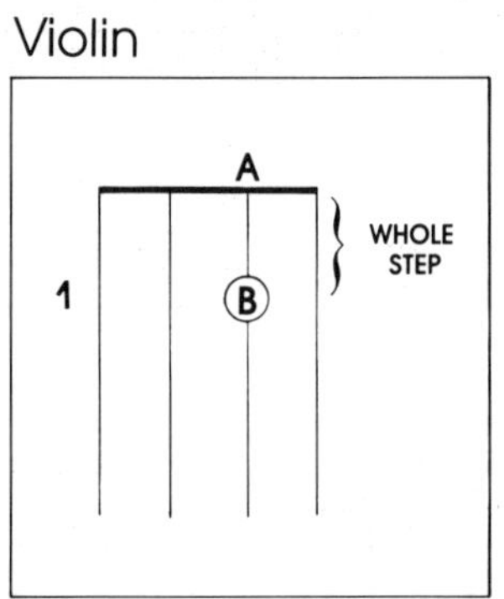

Viola

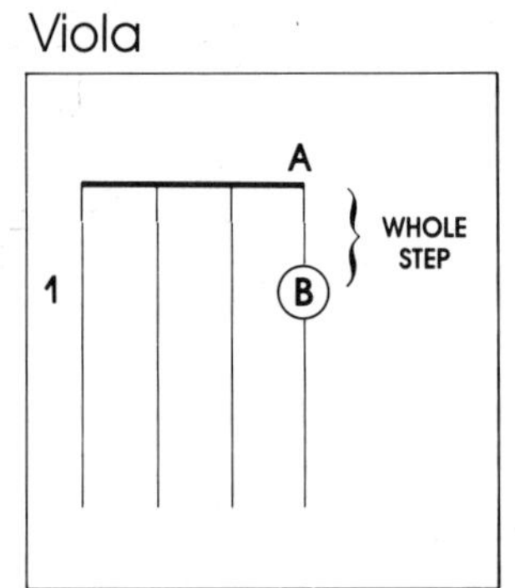

Cello

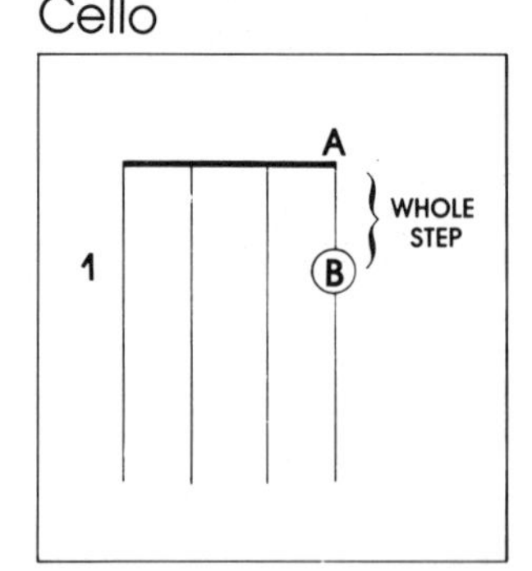

Bass

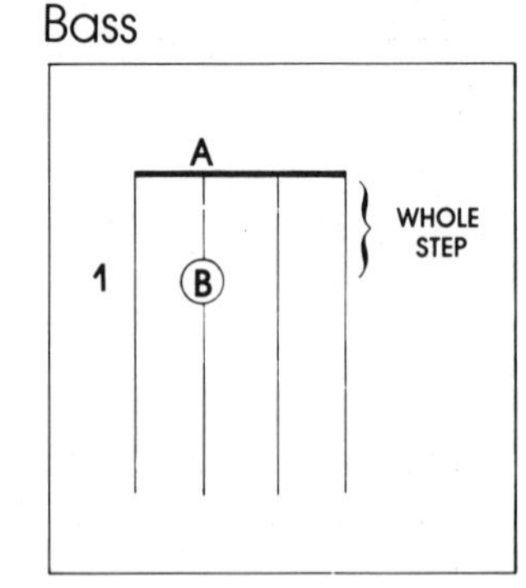

39. NEW NOTES A AND B

| A | B | A | B :‖

40. FOUR NOTES

| D | E | * A | B * :‖

Violin

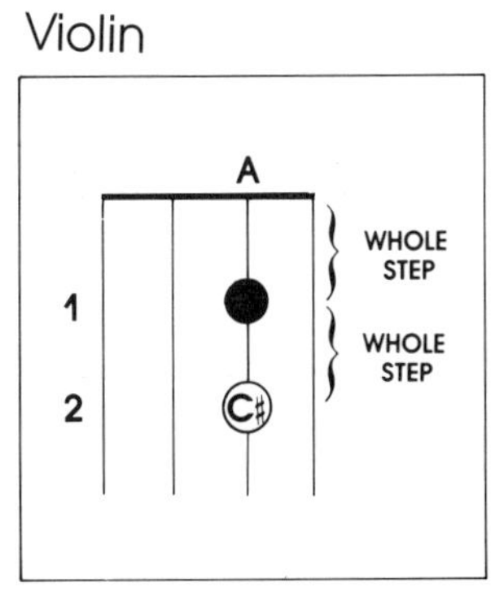

Viola

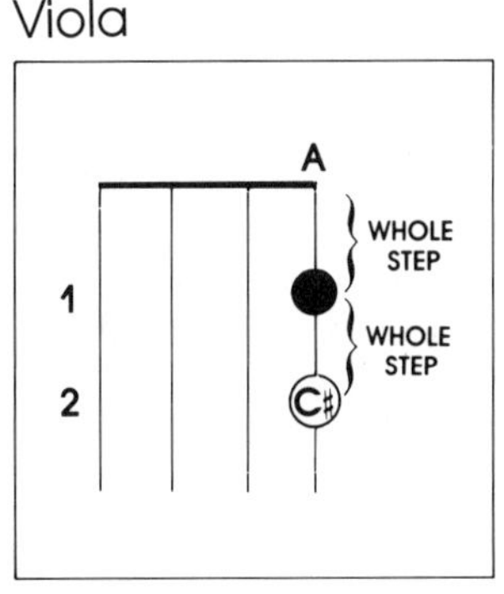

Cello

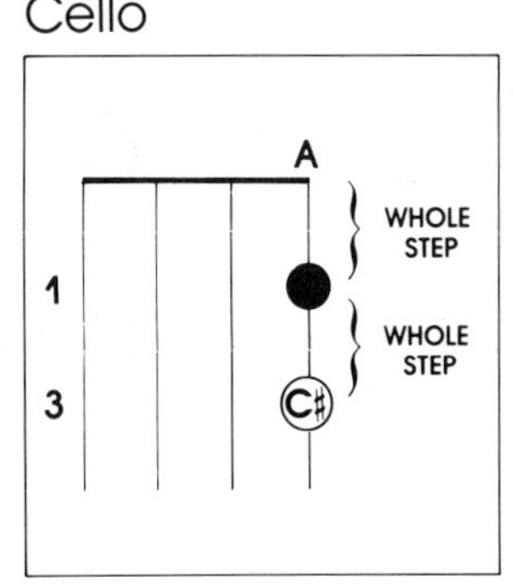

Bass

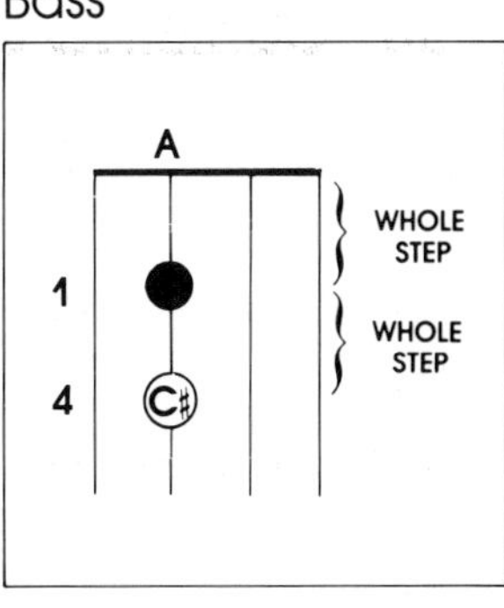

41. UP TO NEW NOTE C♯

| A | B | C♯ | C♯ | B | A :‖

42. SIX NOTES

| D | E | F♯ *| A | B | C♯ *:‖

★ Roll the bow to the new string.

43. FRENCH FOLK SONG

|A A A B |C♯ — B — |A C♯ B B |A ——— |

|A A A B |C♯ — B — |A C♯ B B |A ——— ‖

★ Check your left hand position.

44. HOT CROSS BUNS

|C♯ —— B —— | A —————— | C♯ —— B —— |A —————— |

|A A A A | B B B B | C♯ —— B —— |A —————— ‖

45. MARY HAD A LITTLE LAMB

|C♯ B A B | C♯ C♯ C♯ —— |B B B —— | C♯ C♯ C♯ — |

|C♯ B A B | C♯ C♯ C♯ C♯ |B B C♯ B | A —————— ‖

★ Check your bow grip often.

NEW NOTE

Violin

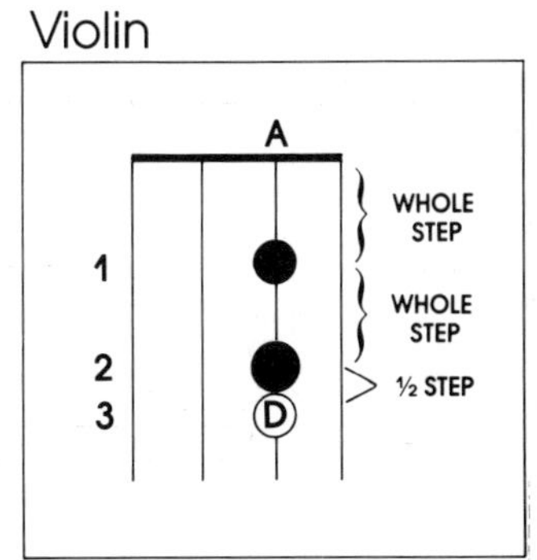

Viola

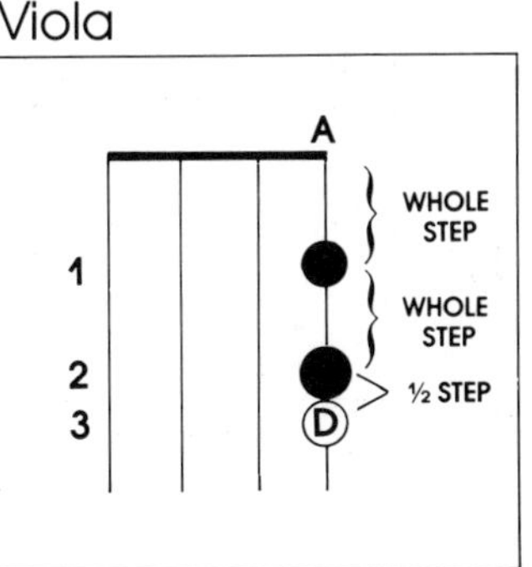

Cello

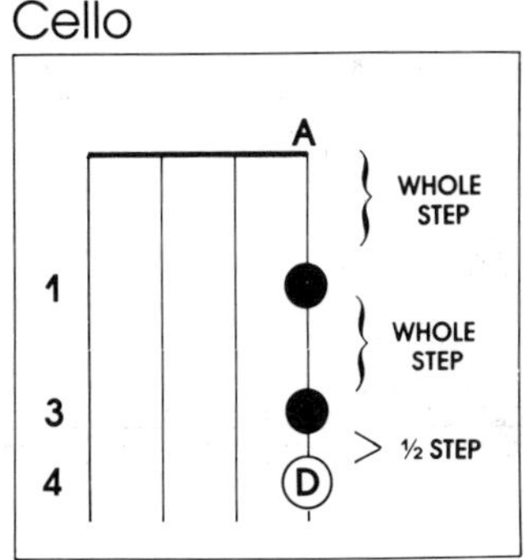

Bass

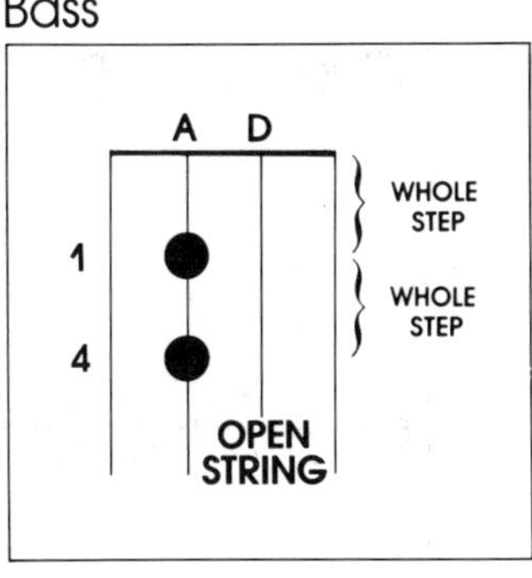

46. TO NEW NOTE D AND BACK

| A | B | C♯ | D | go on:

| D | C♯ | B | A :‖

TEACHER: The concept of tetrachords could be introduced at this time. Refer to the inside front cover for the tetrachord explanation. Be sure to point out that two tetrachords combine to form a major scale.

47. GOING UP THE D MAJOR SCALE

| D (open) | E | F♯ | G |* A | B | C♯ | D* :‖

★ Check your left hand position.

TEACHER: When playing the descending D Major scale, it is important to have students stop and prepare their fingers going from open A to the fingered G. Basses need the same attention going from open G to 4th finger F♯ and open D to the 4th finger C♯. It may be beneficial to have the students actually stop and play the finger preparation. Gradually shorten the time for the preparation until the students can play the descending scale without any stops. This technique will improve the student's intonation.

TEACHER: Students should memorize the D Major scale and apply all Rhythm Patterns from the entire Rote section. Also, be creative and mix the rhythm patterns, i.e. one pattern ascending and another pattern descending, alternate patterns every other measure between two rhythm patterns. Be creative!

48. D MAJOR SCALE-UP AND DOWN

Violin, Viola, Cello

| D (open) | E | F♯ | G |* A | B | C♯ | D |

| D | C♯ | B | A |* Prepare fingers on D E F# G |

| G | F♯ | E | D (open) :‖

Bass

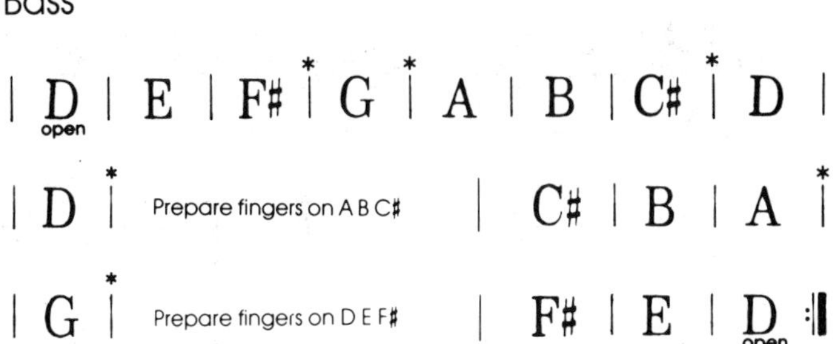

49. Play **ROSIN BOW MARCH, MARCHING SONG** and **CLIMBING UP** on the A string.

TEACHER: This song represents one of the milestones of the beginning stage of development. It offers many opportunities to practice and perfect good bow and finger preparations. The bow preparations are marked with an *. Finger preparations for the note G for violin, viola and cello must be carefully prepared in measures 3, 7, 11 and 15. For bass the F♯ 's in measures 3, 7, 10, 12, and 15 need to be carefully prepared. Also, many well-known variations can go along easily with this song. Students should memorize this song and play it often.

50. TWINKLE, TWINKLE, LITTLE STAR

★ Check your bow grip often.

Below is a listing of all the lines for the next section of this book STARTING BY NOTE. Feel free to duplicate this list and use it for teacher planning or student assignment.

Student Name____________________ School Name____________________

__ 1. D String
__ 2. A String
__ 3. D and A
__ 4. Half Notes
__ 5. Mississippi River
__ 6. Quarters and Halves
__ 7.
__ 8. Rosin Bow
__ 9.
__ 10. Bow Rosin
__ 11.
__ 12. Mixing It Up
__ 13. G String
__ 14.
__ 15. Three Strings
__ 16.
__ 17. C and E Strings
__ 18. Circle of Strings
__ 19. Name Game
__ 20. Mississippi River Duet
__ 21. Tricky Bows
__ 22.
__ 23.
__ 24.
__ 25. Open String Duet
__ 26. New Note E
__ 27.
__ 28.
__ 29. Flashy First
__ 30.
__ 31. Rhythm Teaser
__ 32. New Note F♯
__ 33. Keeping the First Down
__ 34.
__ 35.
__ 36.
__ 37.
__ 38. Mary Had a Little Lamb*
__ 39. Hot Cross Buns*
__ 40. French Folk Song*
__ 41.
__ 42.
__ 43.
__ 44.
__ 45. Name Game
__ 46. New Note G
__ 47. Leave Fingers Down
__ 48. Marching Song*
__ 49. Climbing Up*
__ 50. Keeping Fingers Down
__ 51. Ode to Joy*
__ 52. Notes and Names
__ 53. Counting and Answers
__ 54. Rhythm Teaser
__ 55. Skips
__ 56. More Skips
__ 57. Norwegian Folk Song*
__ 58. Duet in Thirds*
__ 59. Rhythm Teaser
__ 60.
__ 61. Bow Divisions
__ 62. Lightly Row*
__ 63. Pencil Pusher
__ 64. Jingle Bells*
__ 65. New Notes B and C♯
__ 66.
__ 67.
__ 68. French Folk Song (Duet)*
__ 69. Lift Set Game
__ 70. New Note D
__ 71. Tetrachord March*
__ 72. Up the D Major Scale
__ 73. D Scale Round
__ 74. Duet Rhythms for the D Major Scale
__ 75. Concert Song*
__ 76. Technic Trainer No. 1
__ 77. Technic Trainer No. 2
__ 78. Technic Trainer No. 3
__ 79. Two of Us
__ 80. Slow Bows
__ 81. Bohemian Folk Song
__ 82. Twinkle, Twinkle, Little Star*
__ 83. Pencil Pusher
__ 84. O Come, Little Children*
__ 85. D Major Scale in 3
__ 86. D Scale Waltz*
__ 87. Rhythm Teaser
__ 88. Position Check
__ 89. French Folk Song (D Major)*
__ 90. Rhythm Teaser
__ 91. Tricky Melody*
__ 92. Scotland's Burning*
__ 93. Balance the Scale
__ 94.
__ 95.
__ 96.
__ 97.
__ 98. Bow Twister
__ 99.
__100. Go Tell Aunt Rhodie*
__101. It Takes Two*
__102. Slur Three
__103. Hickory Dickory Dock*
__104. Two Step March*
__105. D Arpeggio
__106. Arpeggio March*
__107. The Guiding Hand*
__108. Solo Time*
__109. Pencil Pusher
__110.
__111.
__112. New Notes A, B and C
__113.
__114.
__115. London Bridge*
__116. G Major Scale
__117.
__118. Technic Trainer No. 1
__119. Technic Trainer No. 2
__120. Technic Trainer No. 3
__121. Tonic and Dominant Arpeggios
__122. Peter Peter*
__123. Reuben and Rachel*
__124. Melody for Three Strings*
__125. Three String Madness*
__126. Concert Trio*
__127.
__128. Czech Folk Song*
__129. She'll Be Comin' 'Round the Mountain*
__130. Little Annie*
__131. Rhythm Teaser
__132. Long, Long Ago*
__133. Theme—Beethoven Violin Concerto*
__134. Can-Can*
__135.
__136. N. Paganini*
__137. Kookaburra*
__138. Jolly Old St. Nick*
__139. The Old Woman and the Peddler*
__140. Rhythm Teaser
__141. New Note F♮
__142.
__143.
__144.
__145. Folk Song
__146. Finger Twisters
__147. Keep the Music Ringing*
__148. A Tisket A Tasket*
__149. Hi-Lo No. 1
__150. Hi-Lo No. 2
__151. Musical Road Signs
__152. Mexican Clapping Song/Oh Where Has My Little Dog Gone*
__153. Snake Charmer*
__154. Position Check
__155. New Note C♮
__156.
__157. Some Folks Do*
__158
__159. Bow Twister
__160. Technic Trainer
__161. Finger Twister
__162. Canon*
__163. French Folk Song (C Major)*
__164. Bridge at Avignon*
__165. There's Music in the Air*
__166. Fingering Review
__167. New Notes F♯ and G
__168. New Note A
__169. Technic Trainer
__170. G Major Scale with Broken Thirds
__171. Arpeggio Fun (G Major)*
__172. When Love Is Kind*
__173. Saints*
__174. Skip To My Lou*
__175. Shepherd's Hey*
__176. New Notes C, D and E
__177. New Note F
__178.
__179. C Major Scale With Broken Thirds
__180. Arpeggio Fun (C Major)
__181. Duet In Two Keys*
__182. Theme and Variations*
__183. Happy Blues*
__184. Jazz Feature
__p.48 D Major Scale
__p.48 D Major Broken Thirds
__p.48 G Major Scale
__p.48 G Major Broken Thirds
__p.48 C Major Scale
__p.48 C Major Broken Thirds

*The titles marked with an asterisk (*) have a piano accompaniment in the score and in the Piano Accompaniment book (78PA).

STARTING BY NOTE

THE BASICS

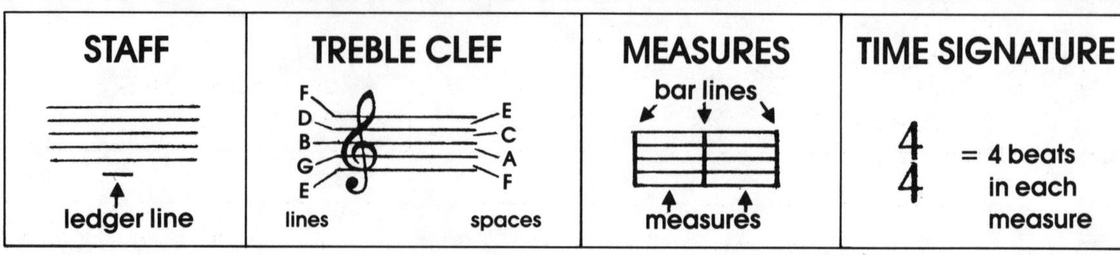

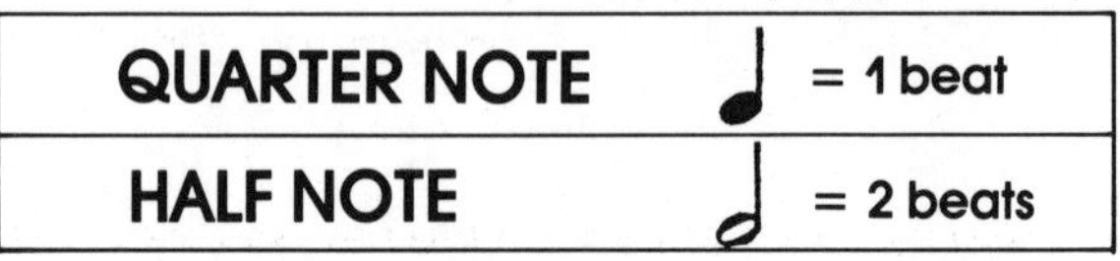

QUARTER NOTE	♩	= 1 beat
HALF NOTE	𝅗𝅥	= 2 beats

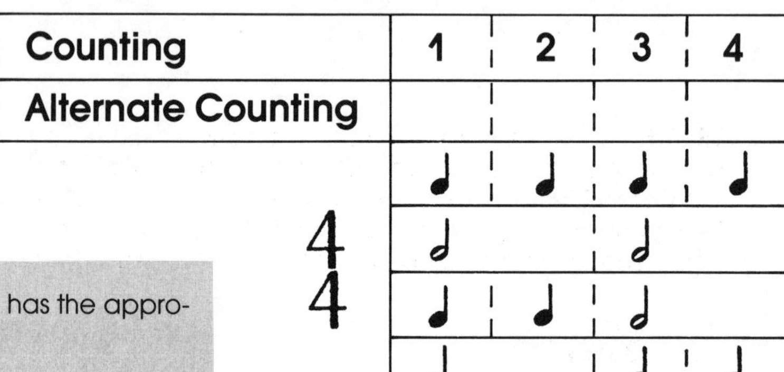

Counting	1	2	3	4
Alternate Counting				

TEACHER: Each student book contains THE BASICS and has the appropriate clef sign indicating the lines and spaces.

NEW NOTES

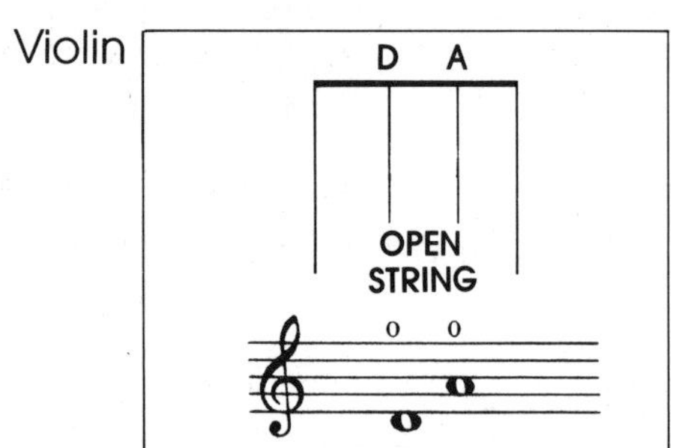

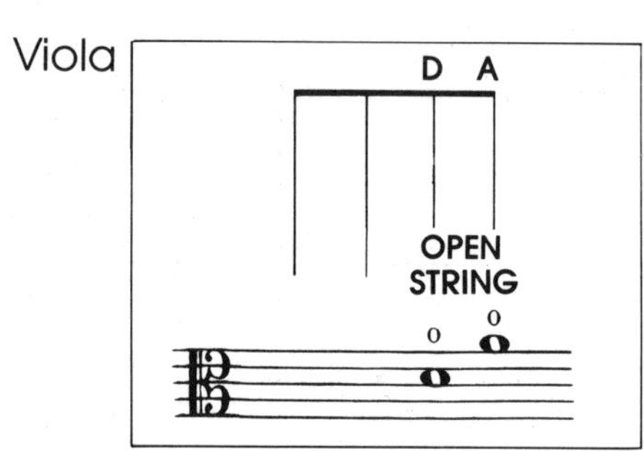

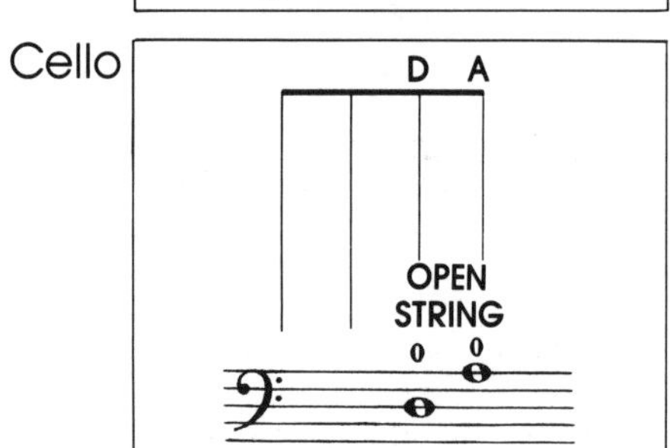

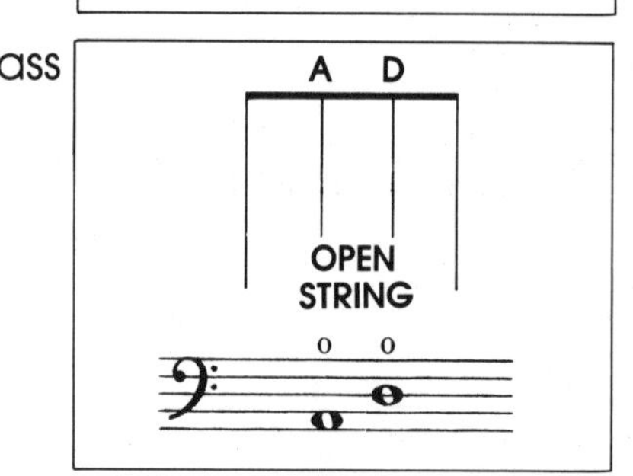

NEW IDEA

STRING LEVEL	Adjust your right arm to play on the correct string.

1. D STRING

2. A STRING

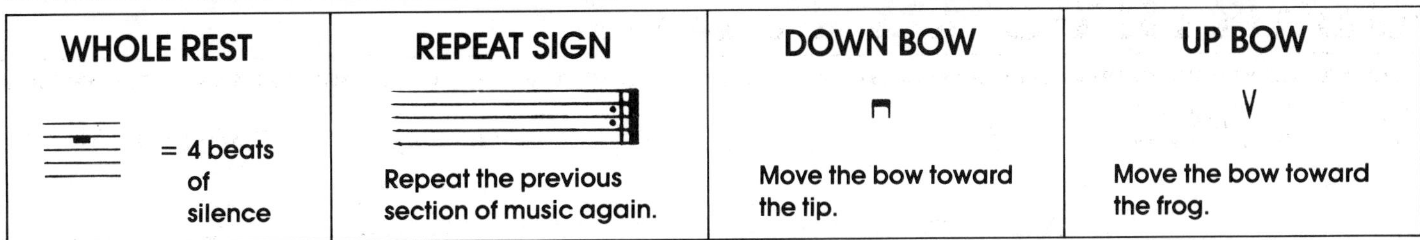

WHOLE REST
= 4 beats of silence
REPEAT SIGN
Repeat the previous section of music again.
DOWN BOW
Move the bow toward the tip.
UP BOW
V
Move the bow toward the frog.

NEW IDEA

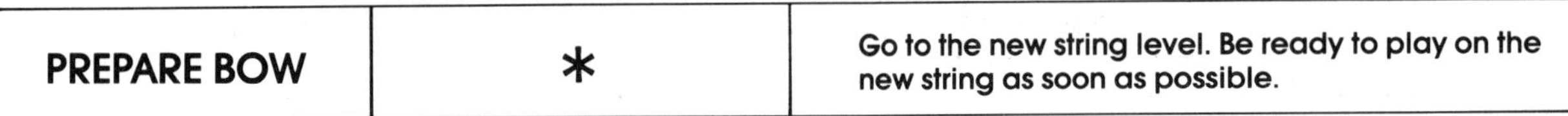

TEACHER: Have all students make good crisp bow preparations so that they are ready to play on the new string as soon as possible. Continue these bow preparations throughout the beginning stages, both in the LEARNING BY ROTE and LEARNING BY NOTE sections. It may be helpful to actually stop at each place in the music that requires a bow preparation (string crossing) and have students execute a well-planned, crisp bow change to the new string level. Emphasize playing on the correct string level with these preparations.

3. D AND A

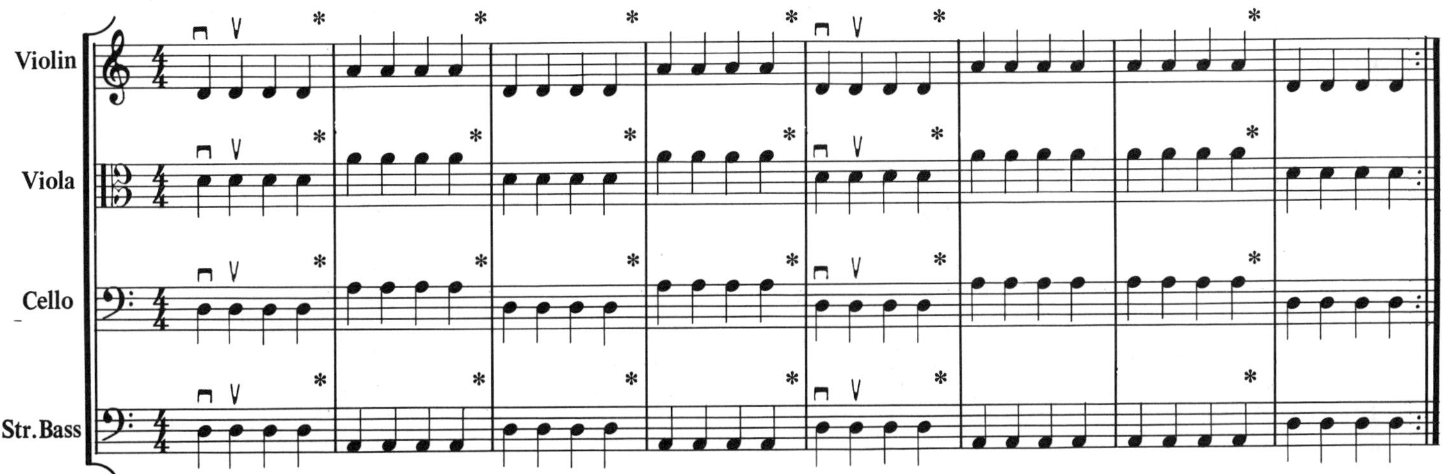

★ Check your bow grip often.

TEACHER: Check the playing positions of your string players often. Have students check each other to make them aware of the important points of holding the bow, holding the instrument, posture and bowing.

4. HALF NOTES

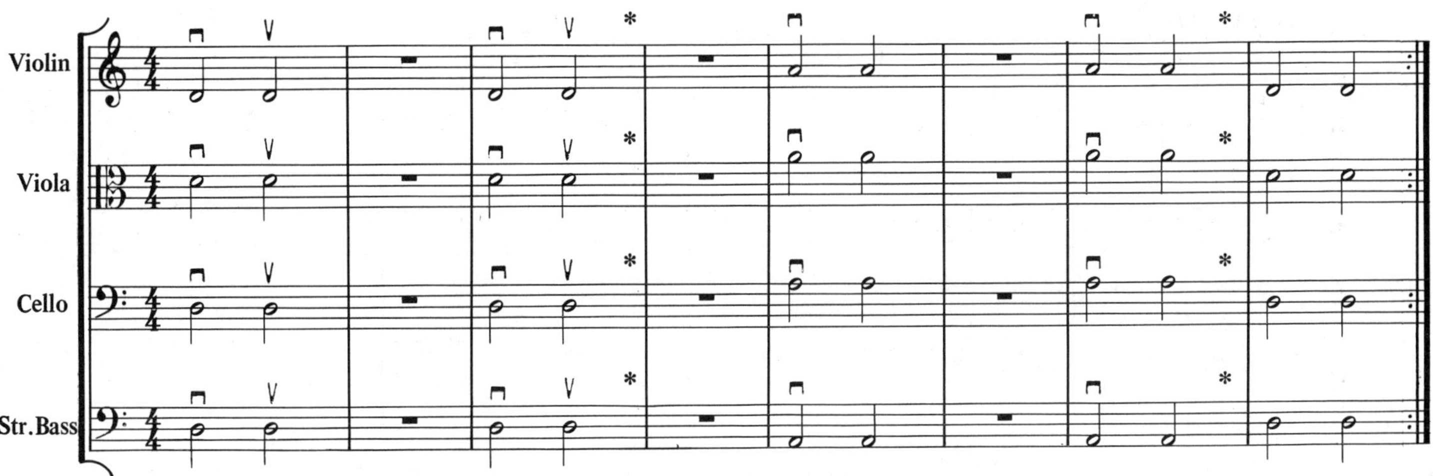

★ Move the bow slower for half notes.

TEACHER: Be sure the students are correctly counting the basic rhythms found in lines 5, 8 and 10. Now is the time to establish a counting system and use it with every line. See Teacher's Manual page 25 for teaching suggestions.

5. MISSISSIPPI RIVER

6. QUARTERS AND HALVES

★ Roll the bow to the new string.

TEACHER: Bow markings are placed in this line to call attention to string changes. Play the line slowly so that the students can execute correct bow direction at each string crossing. Students need to execute good crisp bow preparations at each of these places.

7.

★ Be sure to use fast bow preparations.

8. ROSIN BOW

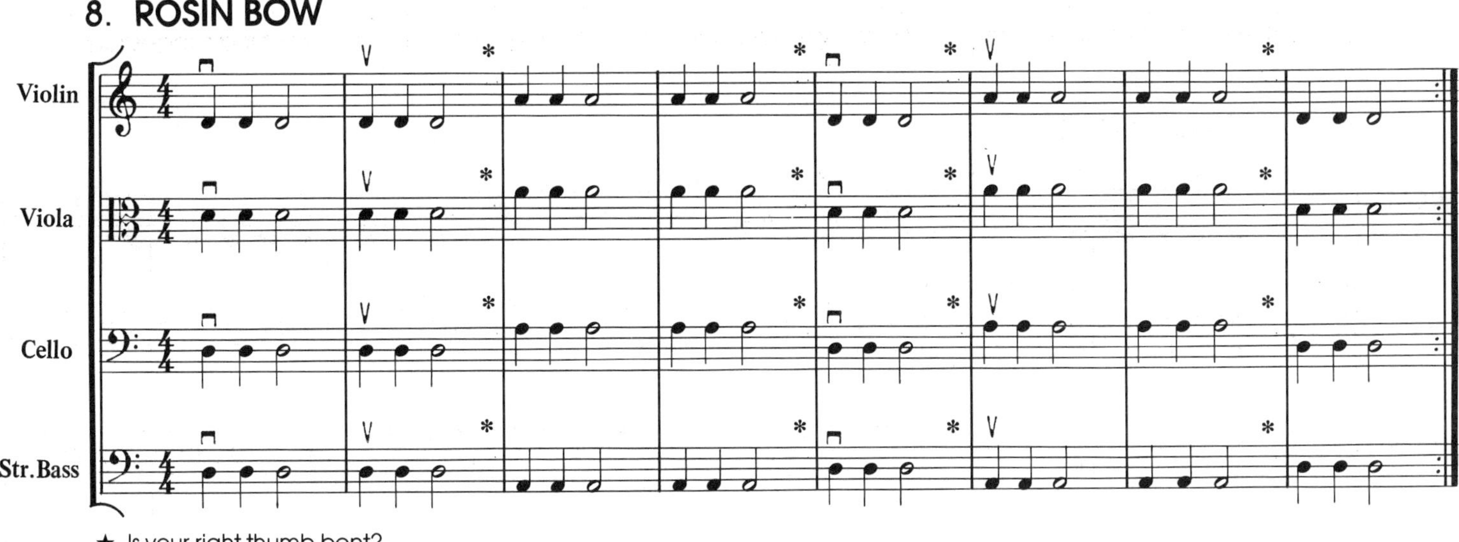

★ Is your right thumb bent?

TEACHER: Have students execute good crisp bow preparations even though they are not marked. Students should be aware that bow preparation marks are not usually marked in music however they still need to be executed for good string crossings.

9.

TEACHER: If students are still having trouble counting the rhythms have them write in the counting for the trouble lines or spots. Have the students play these places pizzicato and count aloud.

10. BOW ROSIN

TEACHER: Exercises 11 and 12 have particularly difficult bow changes.

1. Have the students play these exercises pizzicato so that they are completely sure as to what string they are to play.
2. When playing arco, have the students stop at each * so they can execute a good crisp bow preparation for the new string.

★ Check your bow grip often.

TEACHER: Students must execute good crisp bow preparations even though they are not marked. Explain that bow preparation marks are usually not indicated in the music however they still need to be executed for good string crossing.

★ Roll the bow to the new string.

TEACHER: Assign for home practice the Bow Grip Exercises found on student book page 4, score pages 22-23. String players will build the strength and flexibility that is needed for a good bow grip through the constant repetition of these exercises.

Violin

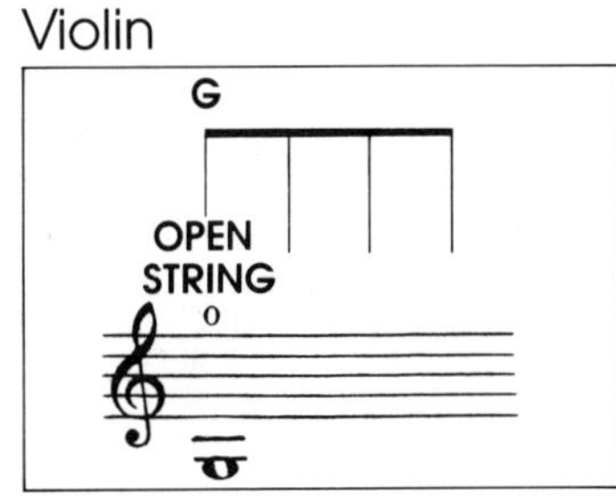

Viola

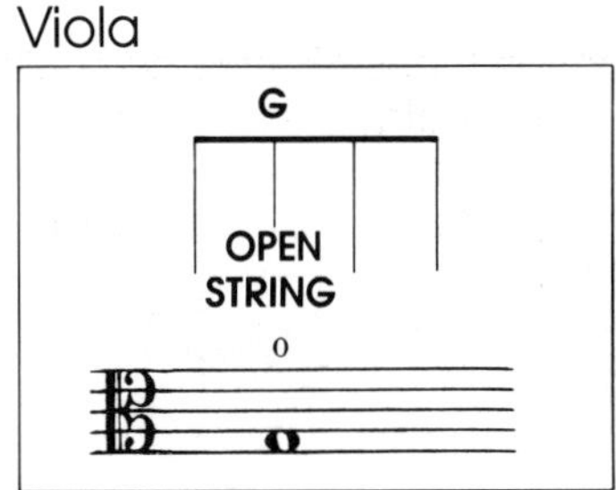

Cello

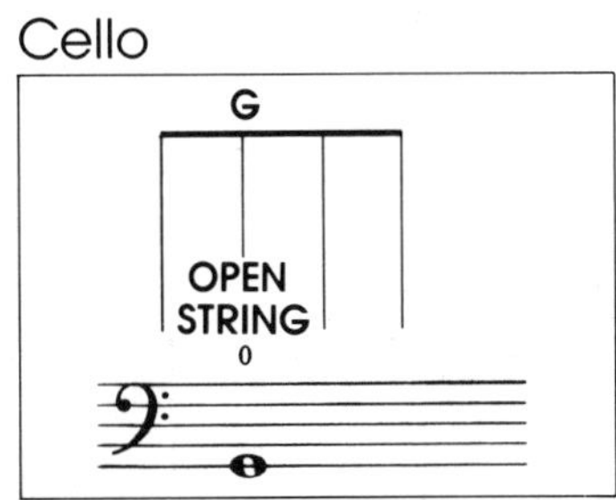

Bass

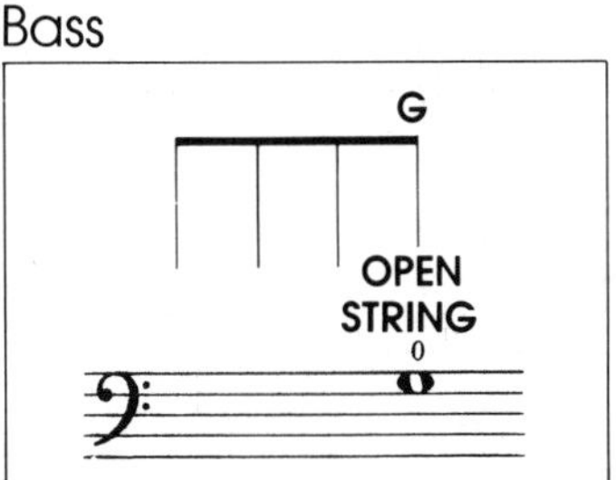

TEACHER: Line 13 is written as two lines in the student books (4 measures in the first line, 4 measures in the second line). Be sure everyone understands to keep playing after the first line and continue playing to the repeat sign.

13. G STRING

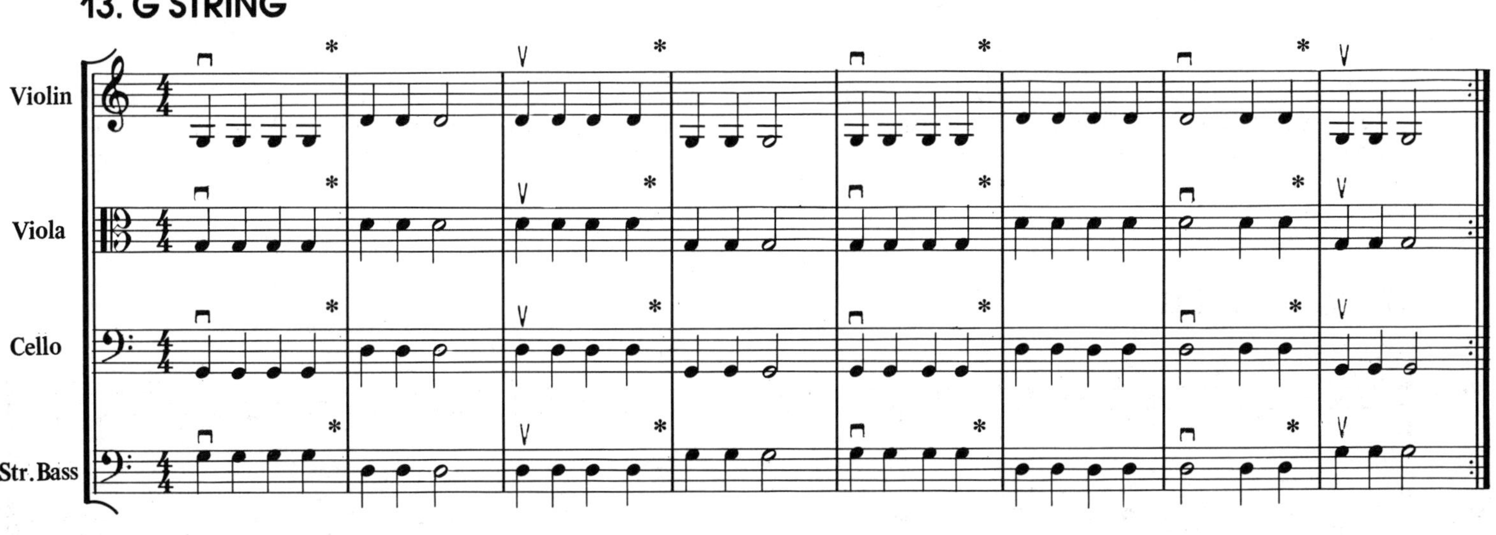

14.

★ Check your bow grip often.

15. THREE STRINGS

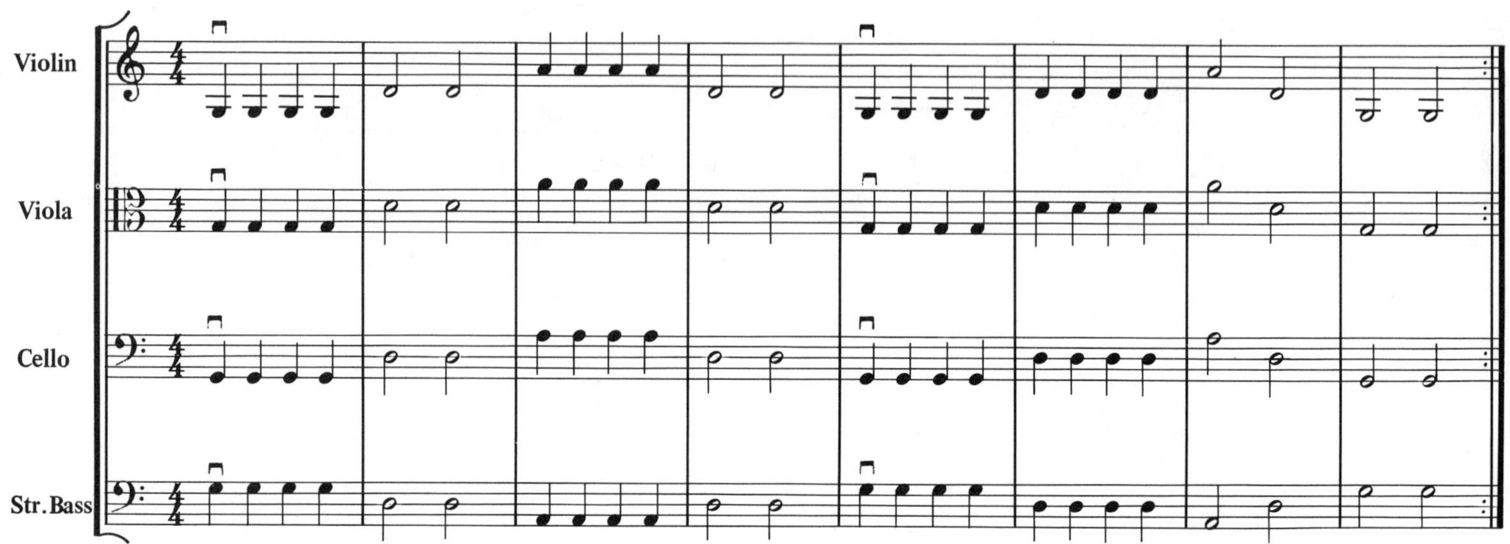

★ Be sure to use fast bow preparations.

TEACHER: Bow markings are placed in this line to call attention to string changes. Play the line slowly so that students can execute the correct bow direction at each string crossing. Students need to execute good crisp bow preparations at each of these places.

16.

TEACHER: Check the playing positions of your string players often. Have students check each other to make them aware of the important points of holding the bow, holding the instrument, posture and bowing. Refer to student book pages 4-5, score pages 14-21 for photos and explanations.

Violin

Cello

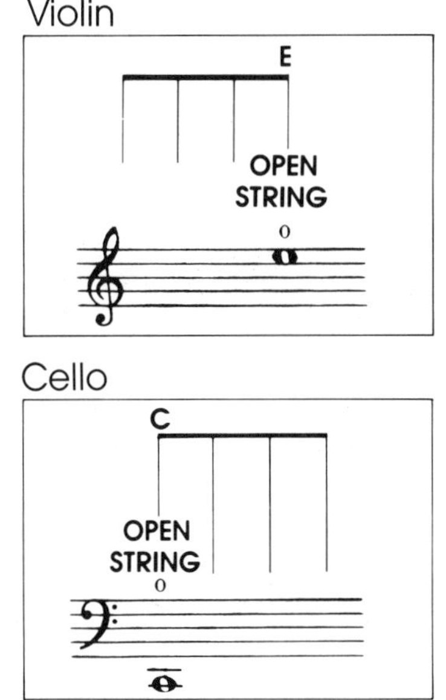

Viola

Bass

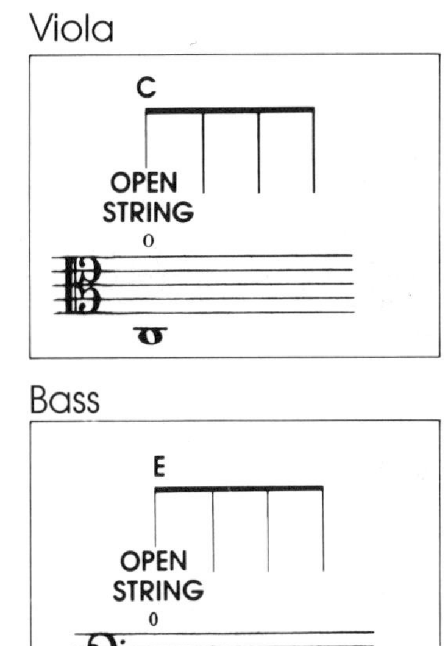

TEACHER: The open E string for violin and bass, and the open C string for viola and cello are introduced simultaneously in line 17. Alert your class that they will be playing in harmony. Also, this exercise is written as two lines in the part books.

17. C AND E STRINGS

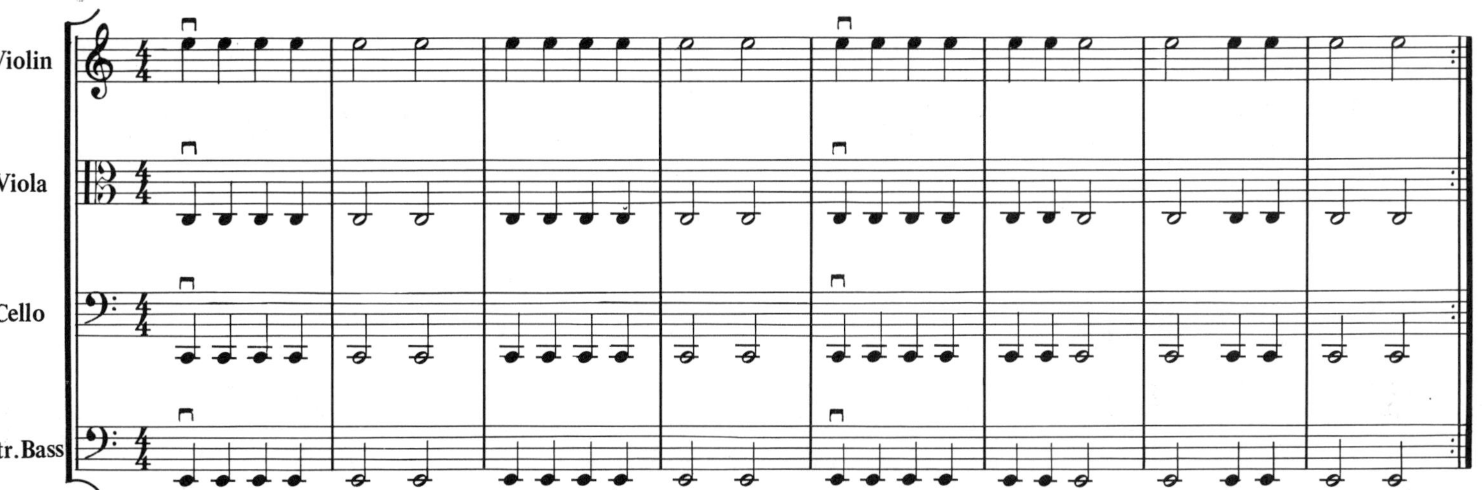

TEACHER: This CIRCLE OF STRINGS is written in harmony; violins and basses on one part, violas and cellos on the other part. Review Line 19 in the Rote section (student book page 8, score page 31) for the CIRCLE OF STRINGS played in unison. Use the CIRCLE OF STRINGS for warm up and for practicing all rhythms and bowings throughout this book.

18. CIRCLE OF STRINGS

★ Raise and lower your arm to the correct level of bowing.

THEORY GAME

19. NAME GAME

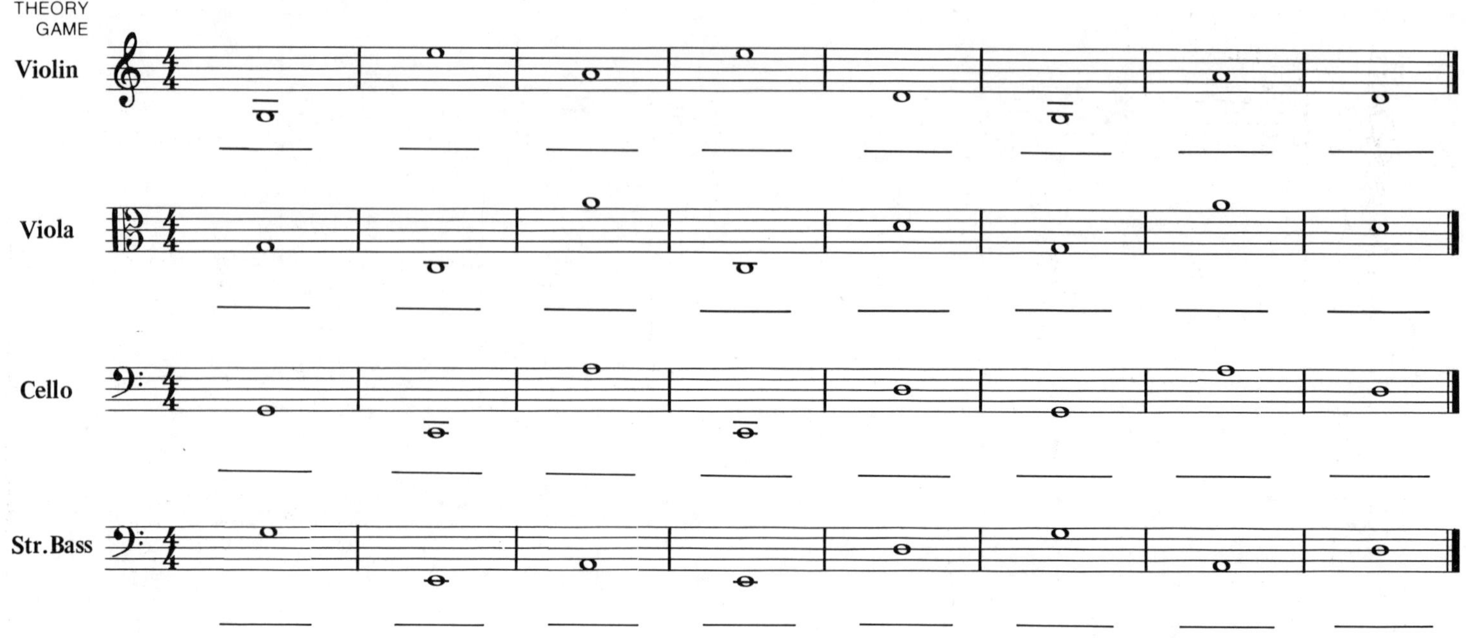

★ Write in the note names.

STUDENT BOOK—Page 17

TEACHER: This duet may also be played as a single unison piece by jumping back and forth between line A and line B.

20. MISSISSIPPI RIVER DUET

TEACHER: This line offers excellent opportunities to practice and develop good crisp string crossings. Many different combinations are presented in this line. Each section should be practiced slowly until it is perfected. Point out the direction of the bow at each string crossing.

21. TRICKY BOWS

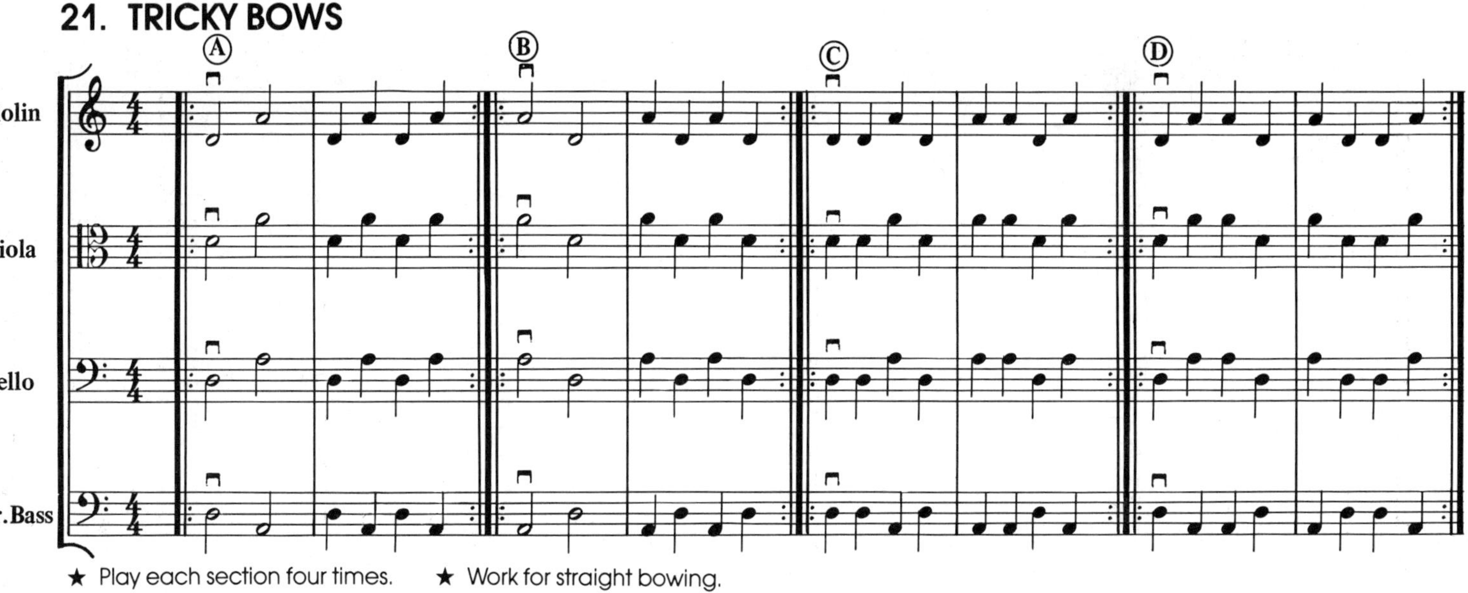

★ Play each section four times. ★ Work for straight bowing.

TEACHER: Line 22 is the circle of strings using the bowing from line 21C. This line is written in harmony.

22.

★ Be sure to use fast bow preparations.

TEACHER: Line 23 is the circle of strings using the bowing from line 21D. This line is written in harmony.

23.

★ Is your right thumb bent?

NEW IDEA

HALF REST

 = 2 beats of silence

Counting	1	2	3	4
Alternate Counting				

THEORY GAME

24.

Violin
Viola
Cello
Str. Bass

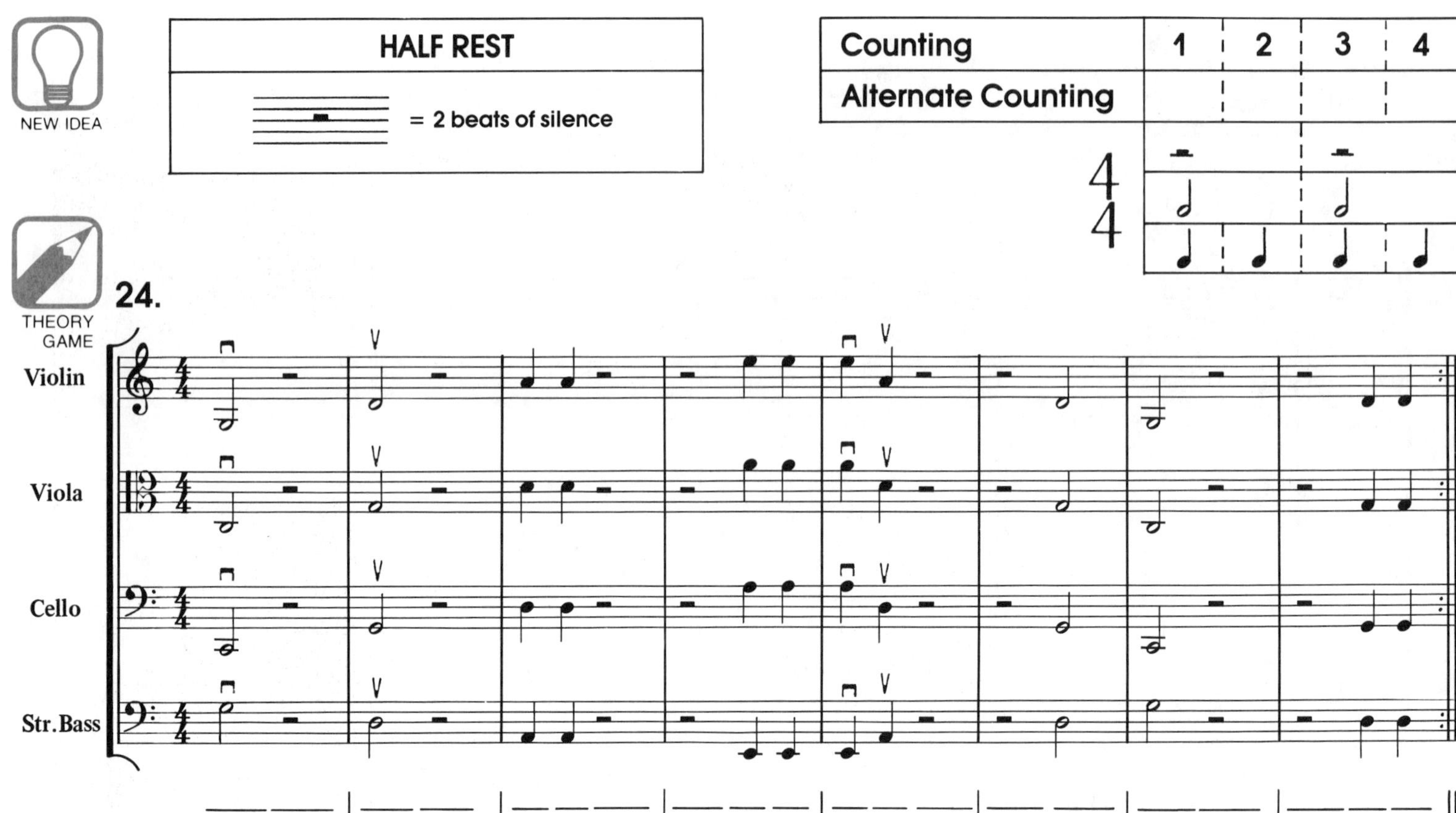

★ Write in the counting.

TEACHER: Explain the meaning of duet. This is the first time that parts played by other instruments are not shown in their music. This is the way orchestra music is printed.

25. OPEN STRING DUET—with cellos and basses

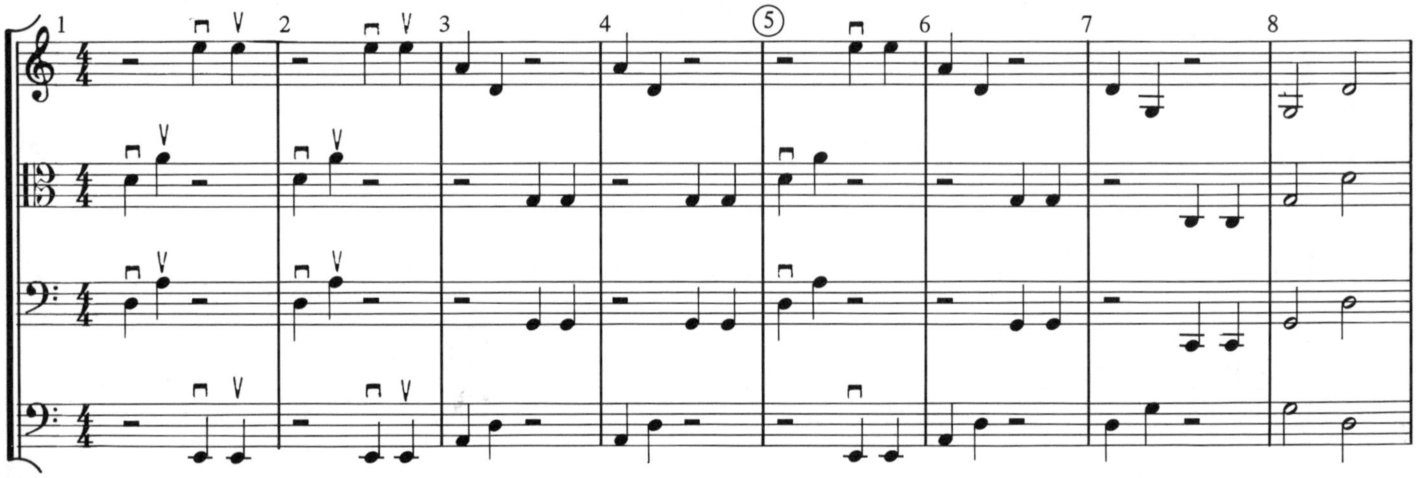

Violin
Viola
Cello
Str. Bass

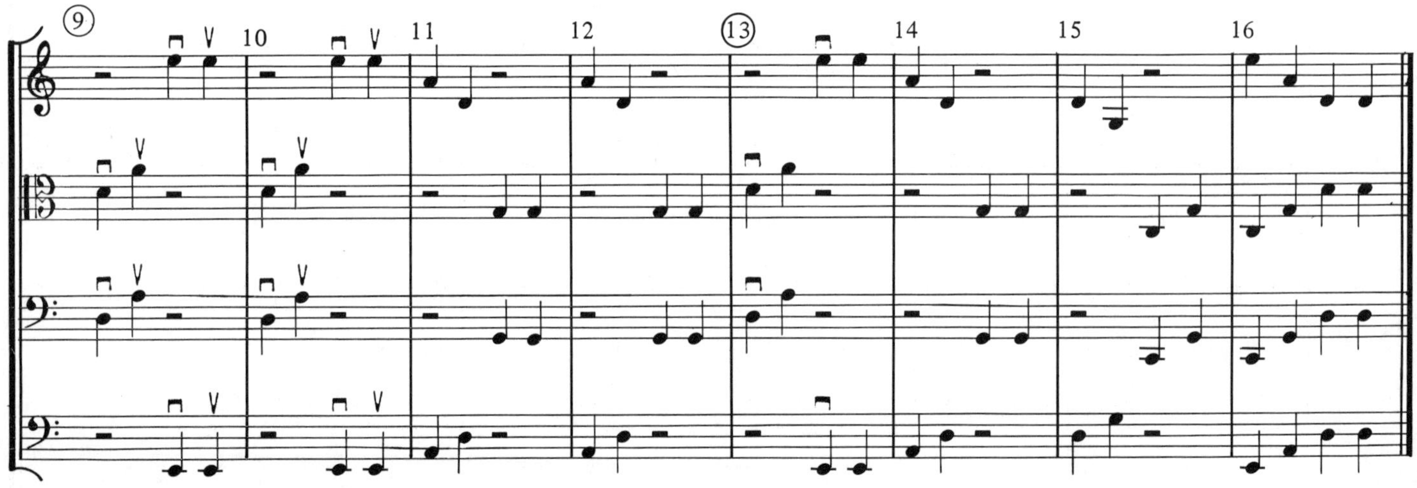

Vln.
Vla.
Cello
Str. Bass

★ Also play this duet pizzicato.

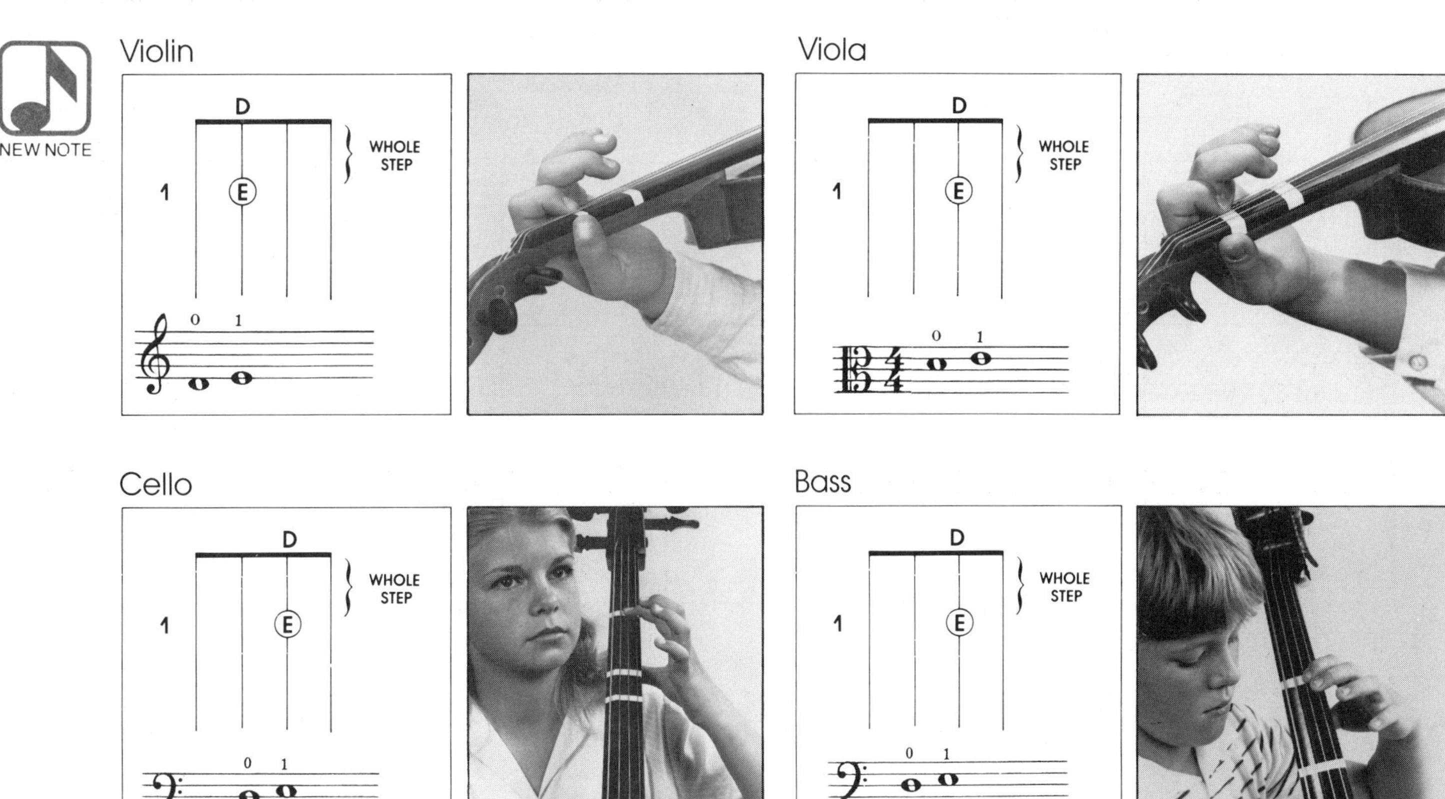

26. NEW NOTE E

(A)

Violin

Viola

Cello

Str. Bass

★ Prepare your first finger during the rests.

(B)

Violin

Viola

Cello

Str. Bass

27.

28.

★ Check your bow grip often.

29. FLASHY FIRST

TEACHER: Students must keep their first finger down on the D string when playing open A. This is a very important intonation technique. This technique can be introduced by having the students place their 1st finger on the D string and then plucking the open A string. Then check the student for correct placement of the finger (including the angle of the finger to the string, curvature of the finger, and the position of the left arm and hand).

★ Keep your first finger down where indicated.

31. RHYTHM TEASER

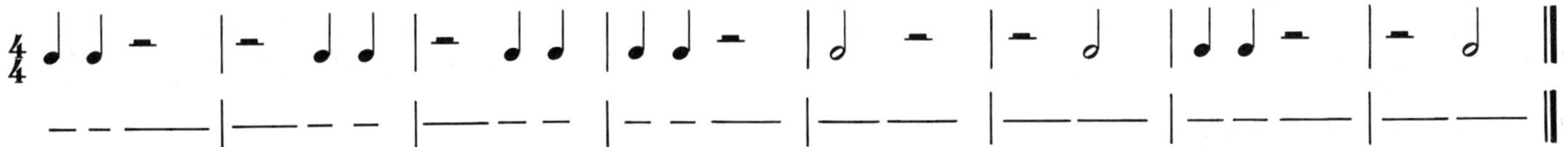

1. Write in the counting. 2. Clap and count. 3. Play arco or pizzicato.

TEACHER: STRING TEACHER'S SURVIVAL KIT

1. Tool or bent pin to tighten chin rests
2. Screwdriver or Roth tool to adjust patent pegs
3. Small needle nose pliers to adjust fine tuners
4. Tweezers to pull strings through pegs
5. Pliers or wrench to tighten music stands
6. Peg dope
7. Bow lubricant (graphite) for fine tuners and bow screw
8. Fingernail clippers
9. Marking tape or dots for finger placement aids or bow division markings
10. Rubber bands for shoulder pads
11. Extra strings (Violin E's, Violin, Viola and Cello A's)
12. Set of books
13. Sound post setter
14. 0000 steel wool to clean rosin from strings
15. Sense of humor!

Violin

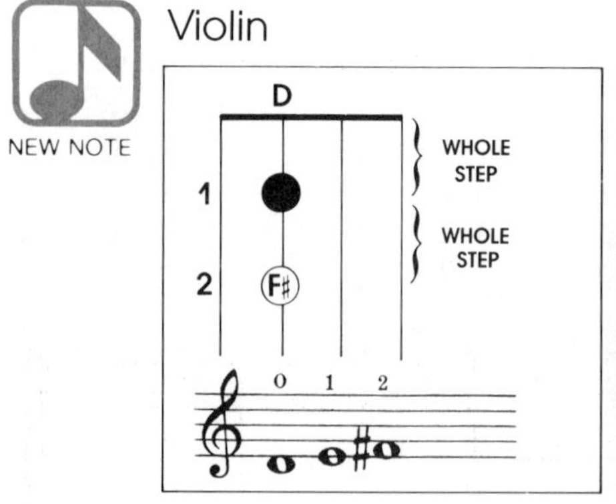

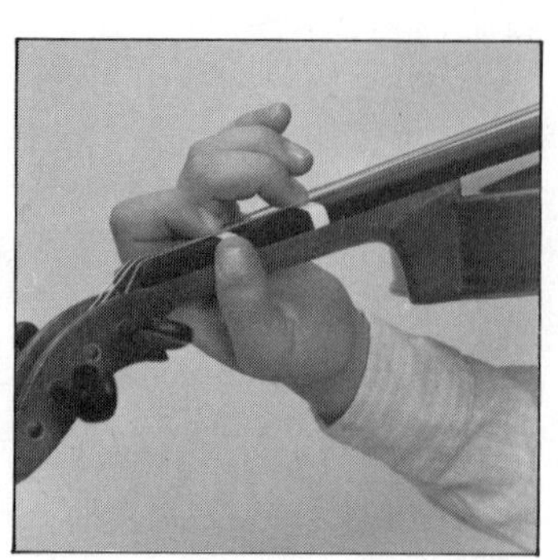

Viola

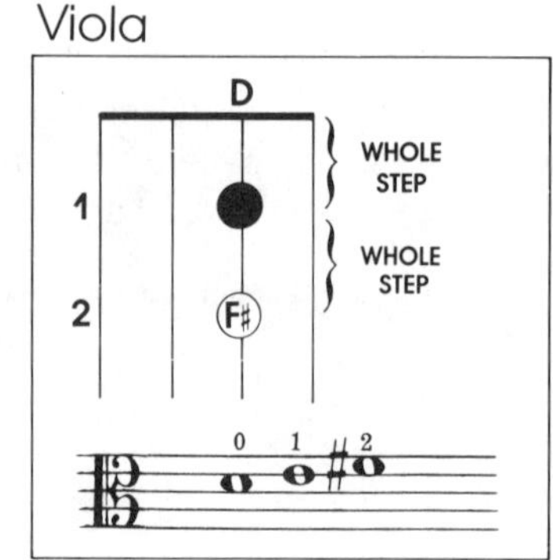

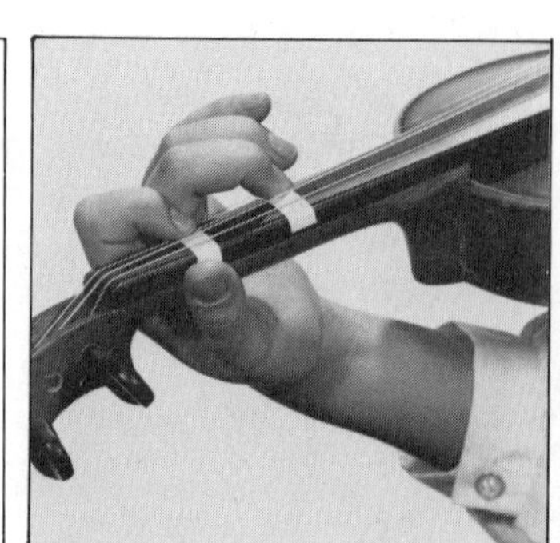

Cello

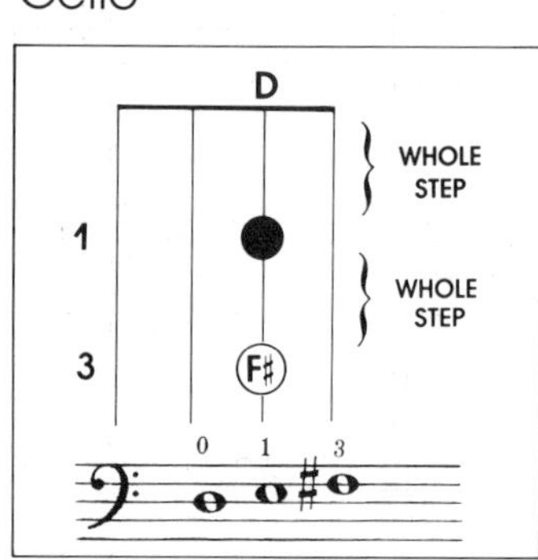

Bass

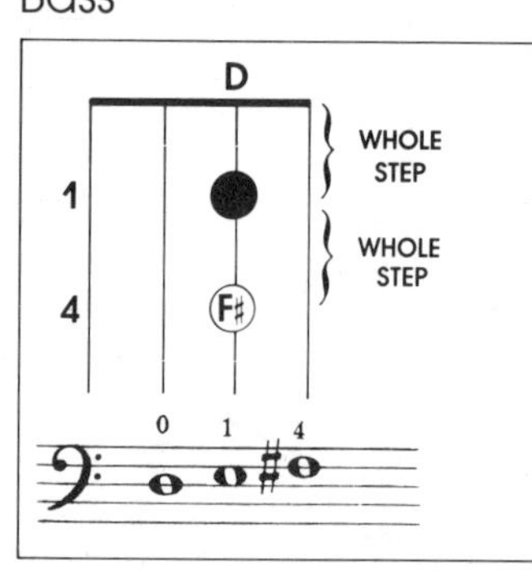

TEACHER: Remind students to hold the following fingers down as they play F♯: Violin and Viola–1st finger
Cello–1st and 2nd finger
Bass–1st, 2nd and 3rd finger

32. NEW NOTE F♯

★ Prepare the next finger during the rest.

TEACHER: Be sure students do not lift their first finger when playing F♯. Check the left hand thumb position of the cello and bass players often. The thumb must be behind the 2nd finger.

33. KEEPING THE FIRST DOWN

Violin
★ Keep your first finger down when placing the second finger.
Viola
★ Keep your first finger down when placing the second finger.
Cello
★ Keep your first finger down when placing the third (and second) finger.
Str. Bass
★ Keep your first finger down when placing the fourth (second and third) finger.

34.

Violin

Viola

Cello

Str. Bass

35.

Violin

Viola

Cello

Str. Bass

★ Keep your fingers arched above the string ready to play.

PREPARE FINGERS	To accurately play notes that involve a skip or an interval, put the finger(s) down on the notes between the interval or written notes.

TEACHER: One of the most important keys to good intonation at the beginning stage is the preparation of fingers. For example, to go from one note to another that involves a skip, have the student put down (and sometimes play) the note(s) between the skip rather than the student arbitrarily placing a finger and hoping that it lands in the correct place. Many repetitions of scale-like preparations will improve the correct finger spacing necessary for the good intonation of passages with skips. Line 36 has three opportunities to use this important technique.

1. Prepare the F♯ at the beginning by playing the notes in parenthesis.
2. Prepare the skip from open D to F♯ by playing the notes in parenthesis in measures 3 and 6.

Students should look for opportunities to prepare fingers in every exercise and song to improve their intonation.

36.

37.

★ Prepare your fingers between D and F♯.

TEACHER:
Musical Position Game
This is a fun game for orchestra students and helps to break up the normal routine of class activities. It can be played at any stage of the students' development. Instruct students as you start that they will be playing one of their favorite songs. While they are playing, you will give them a signal to stop. The signal can be given by a hand clap or by a word signal such as "freeze". All players must stop immediately and not move as you check for a predetermined position item. Anyone who is caught in error is out and the game resumes until the final winner is selected.

The following items form a basic check-list:

1. right thumb bent on bow
2. proper placement of pinkie finger (R.H.)
3. proper placement of left thumb
4. left wrist and arm in straight line
5. proper position of left elbow
6. proper instrument position
7. correct posture (sitting or standing)
8. a straight bow stroke (between bridge and fingerboard)
9. correct finger placement (correct pitch)
10. curved fingers (L.H.) (the fingertips placed on the string)

38. MARY HAD A LITTLE LAMB

Traditional

TEACHER: Rosin has a tendency to build up on the strings if not wiped off after each playing session with a soft rag. This rosin build up which has an adverse effect on tone production can easily be removed by using 0000 steel wool. Alcohol is not as good as it will absorb the rosin and deposit it in the string windings.

BOW LIFT	ʼ	Lift the bow and return it to the lower half or frog. Start the new bow stroke down (⊓) bow.

TEACHER: Check the bow lifts. Be sure everyone uses a circular motion above the string and places the bow gently on the string. Be sure the half note is held full value before the bow lift. Suggest to students the feeling of moving the bow away from the body on the note before the bow lift. This helps to counteract the motion of pulling back from the shoulder in anticipation of the bow lift.

TEACHER: This duet may also be played as a single unison piece by reading back and forth between line A and line B.

39. HOT CROSS BUNS

Traditional-Duet

Ⓐ Violin, Viola, Cello, Str. Bass

Ⓑ Violin, Viola, Cello, Str. Bass

Piano

40. FRENCH FOLK SONG

TEACHER: This is another opportunity to leave fingers down on one string while playing on another string. Practice Line 41 pizzicato so that students can concentrate on left hand technique. In addition, string players should place the bow very gently after each indicated bow lift. Play this line using the written rhythms on the open D string so that students can concentrate on right hand technique of lifting, returning to the frog and placing the bow gently on the string.

41.

★ Place the bow down gently after you lift.

TEACHER: Bow check—Students often forget to loosen their bows after they have been playing. Make a game of checking bows before class starts or after the students have packed up to see if bows have been put away properly without tension.

42.

★ Check your left hand position.

43.

TEACHER: Many string players go through the motion of rosining their bows but are not very successful in applying enough rosin to make a solid tone. Perhaps a little extra help in the technique of rosining is appropriate at this time. Check the rosin to see if it shows signs of being used. Extra effort is needed to use a newly haired bow on a new cake of rosin. You may need to scar the surface of the new rosin cake. In round cakes of rosin, work the bow around in a circular pattern to evenly wear the rosin.

44.

Violin
Viola
Cello
Str. Bass

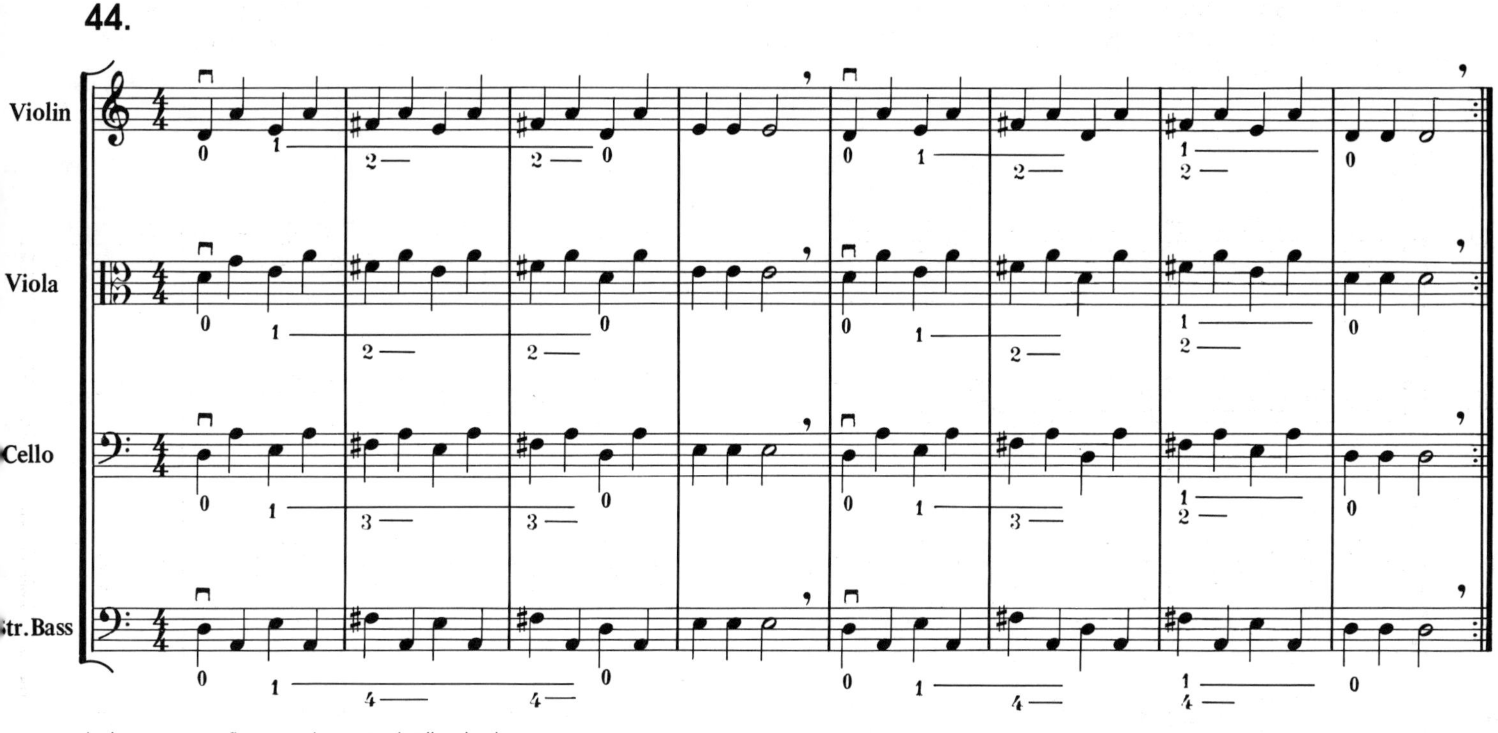

★ Leave your fingers down as indicated.

TEACHER: Students need constant reinforcement of note names. NAME GAME provides this opportunity and can also be used as a reference guide.

HEORY GAME

45. NAME GAME

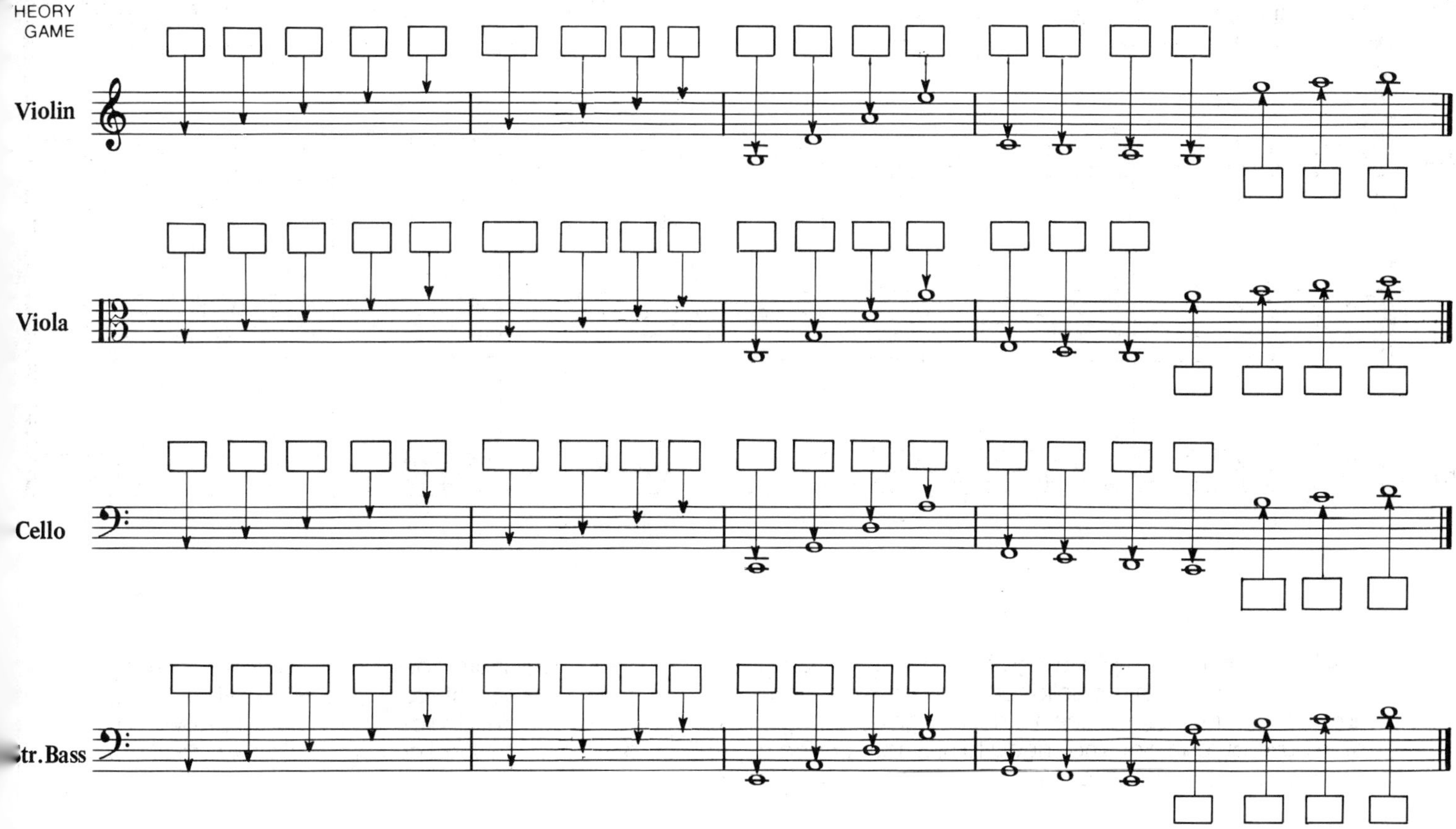

Violin
Viola
Cello
Str. Bass

★ Write the name of the line, space or note in the box at the end of each arrow.

NEW NOTE

Violin

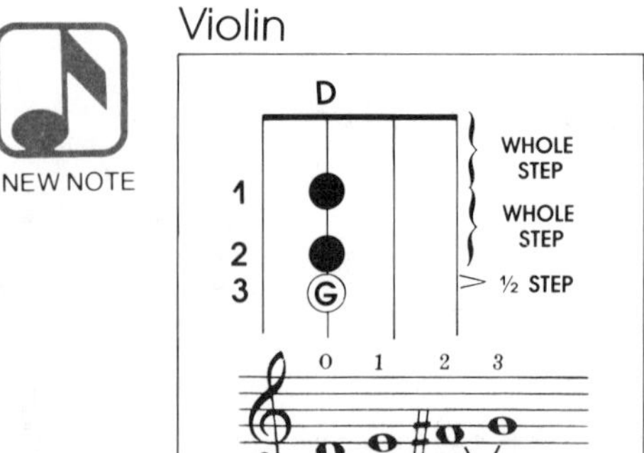

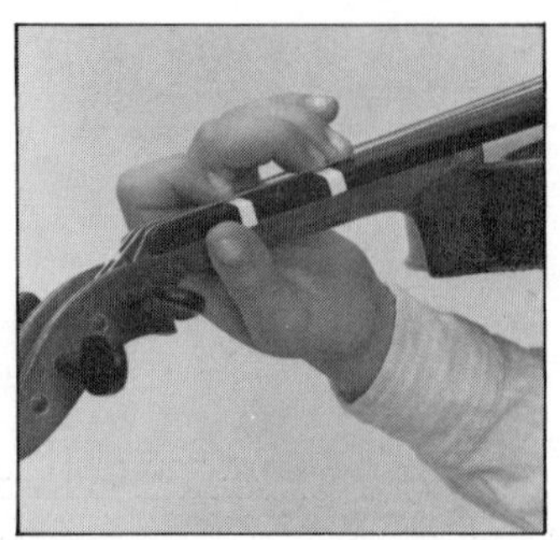

Viola

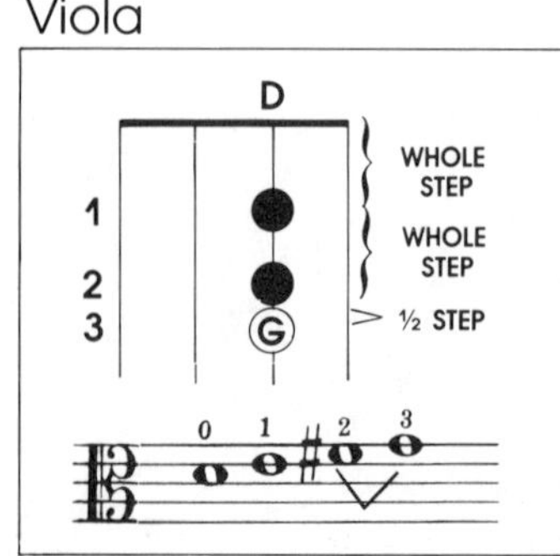

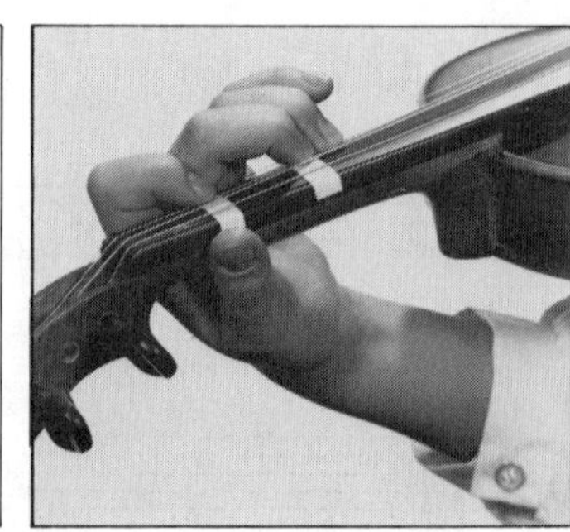

Cello

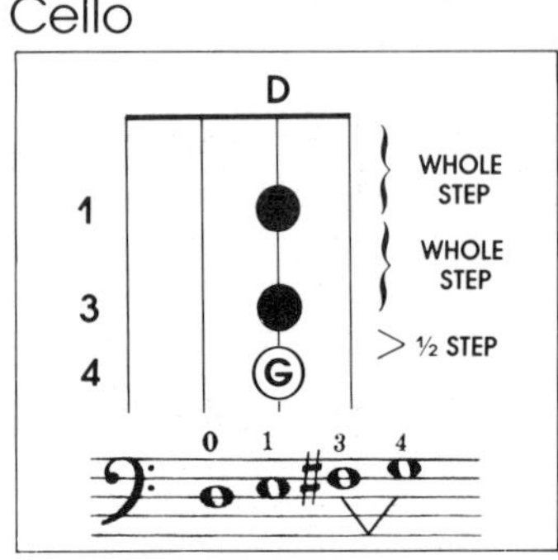

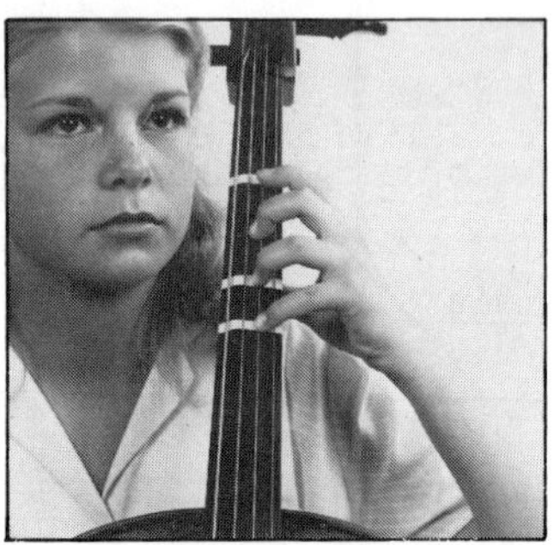

Bass

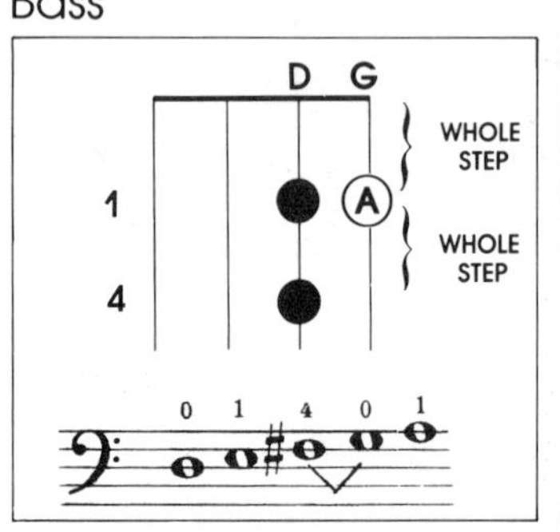

The string bass student book does not show a photo here.

TEACHERS: Putting more than one finger down will help hold the string against the fingerboard for a clearer tone.
Violins and Violas—The 1st and 2nd fingers must be down to clearly play F♯.
Cellos—The 1st, 2nd and 3rd fingers must be down to clearly play F♯.
Basses—The 1st, 2nd, 3rd and 4th fingers must be down to clearly play F♯. You may want to put a rubber band around the 2nd, 3rd and 4th fingers to emphasize and train these fingers to stay together and to stress a big space between the 1st and 2nd fingers.

46. NEW NOTE G

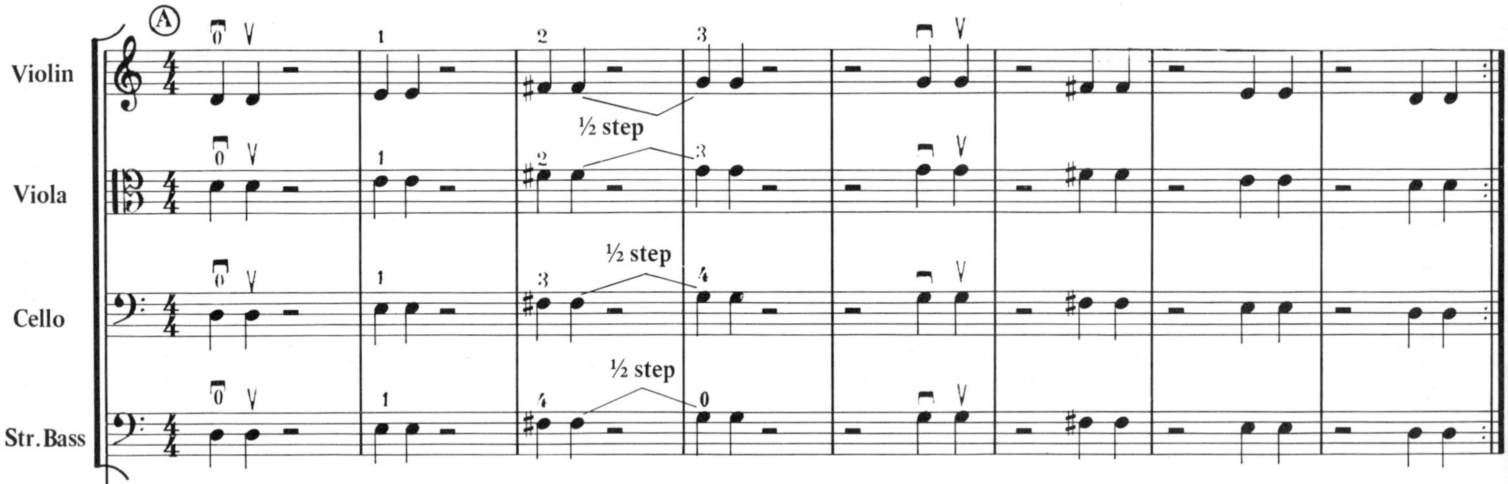

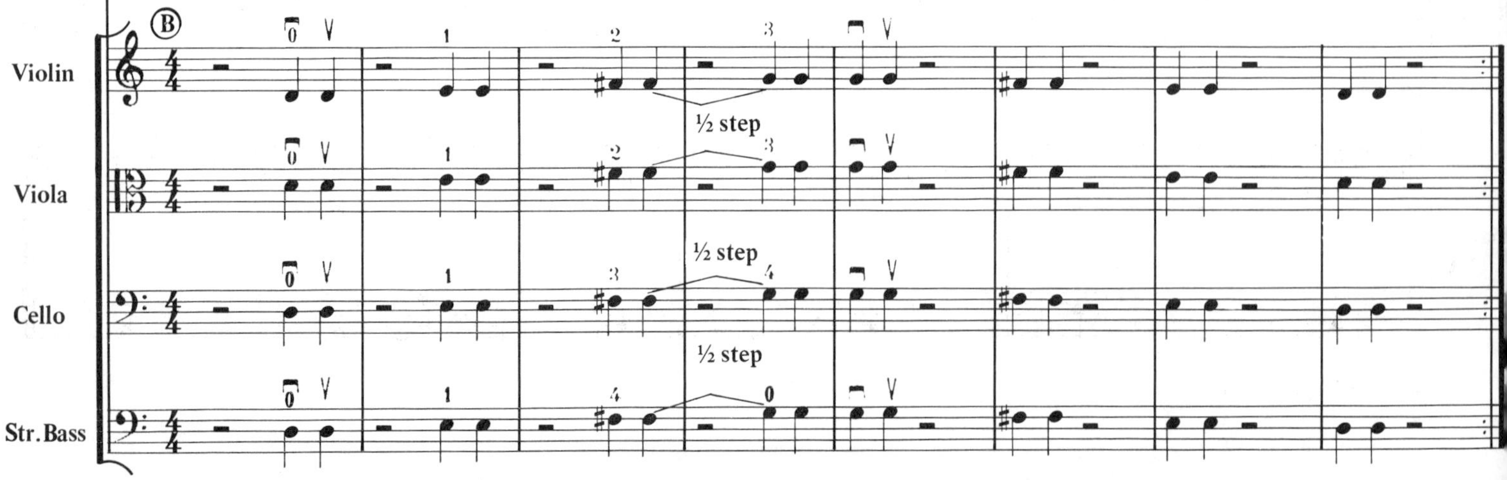

(A)

Violin — 0 1 2 ½ step 3

Viola — 0 1 2 ½ step 3

Cello — 0 1 3 ½ step 4

Str. Bass — 0 1 4 ½ step 0

(B)

Violin — 0 1 2 ½ step 3

Viola — 0 1 2 ½ step 3

Cello — 0 1 3 ½ step 4

Str. Bass — 0 1 4 ½ step 0

TEACHER: On Lines 47-51, have the students leave fingers down where possible. This is a very important technique for good intonation.

47. LEAVE FINGERS DOWN

Violin
Viola
Cello
Str. Bass

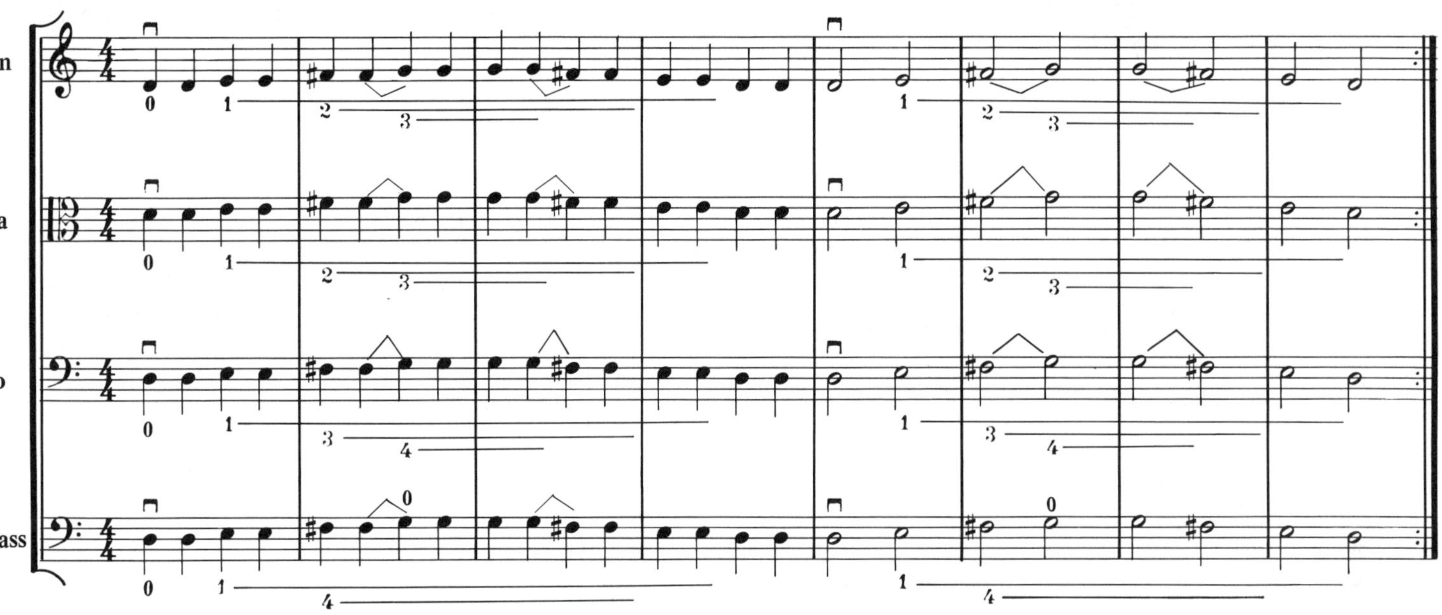

48. MARCHING SONG

Violin
Viola
Cello
Str. Bass
Piano

★ Check your bow grip often.

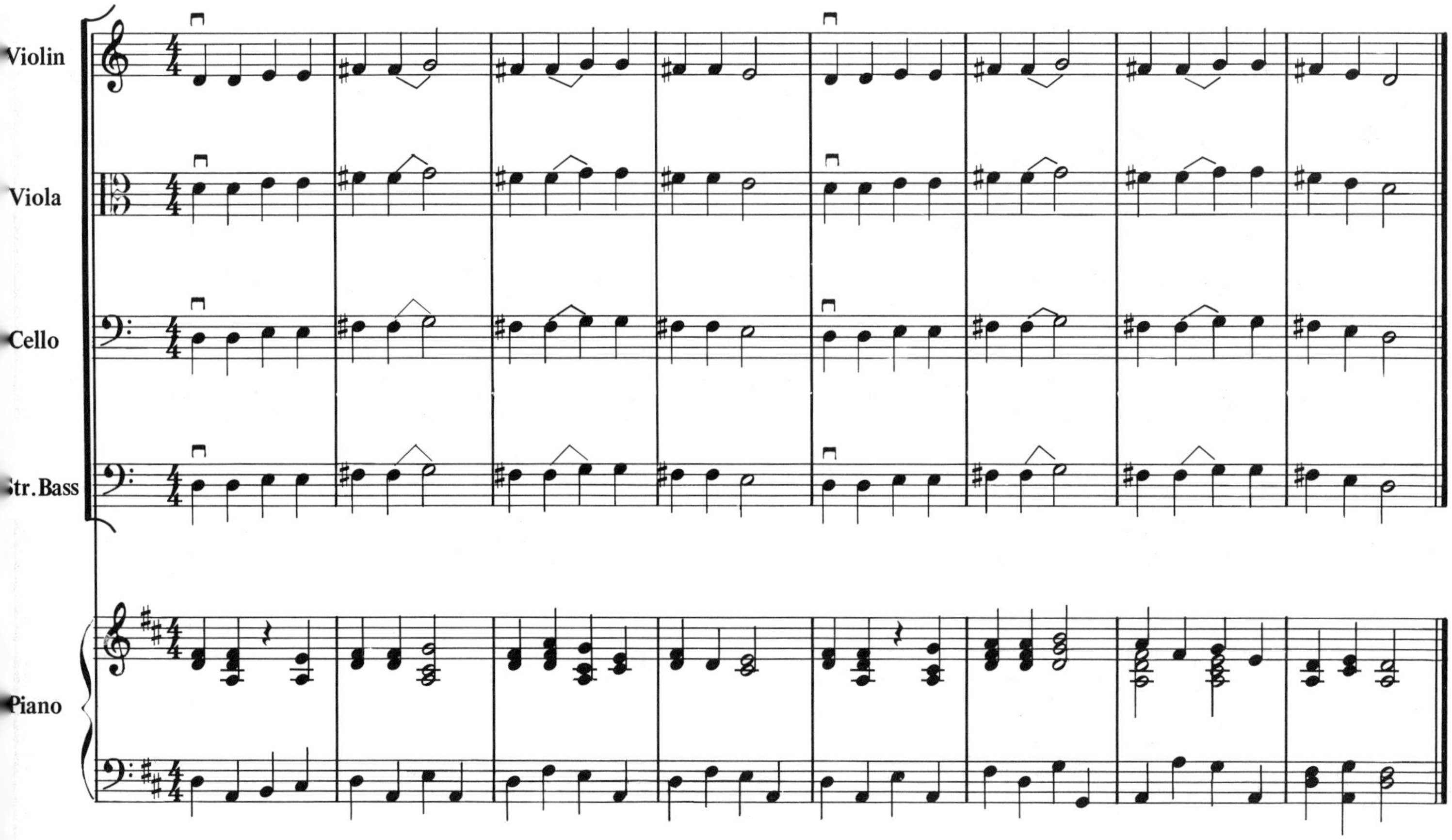

TEACHER: MARCHING SONG and CLIMBING UP are identical to those found in the STARTING BY ROTE section. Students might enjoy playing them from the rote section to see how far they have progressed in note reading.

49. CLIMBING UP

★ Check your left hand position.

TEACHER: This is the first experience for bass players to play 1st finger A on the G string. Refer the students to the diagram at the top of student book page 21 showing proper finger placement for the note A on the G string.

50. KEEPING FINGERS DOWN

★ This is new note A for the string bass.

51. ODE TO JOY
Beethoven
Violin
Viola
Cello
Str. Bass
Piano
TEACHER: Students may use Line 45 for a reference.
THEORY GAME
52. NOTES AND NAMES
Violin
a g e
c a f e
b a d g e
d e f a c e d
Viola
a g e
c a f e
b a d g e
d e f a c e d
Cello
a g e
c a f e
b a d g e
d e f a c e d
Str. Bass
a g e
c a f e
b a d g e
d e f a c e d
★ Draw the notes as indicated in measures 1, 3, 5 and 7. Name the notes in measures 2, 4 and 6.

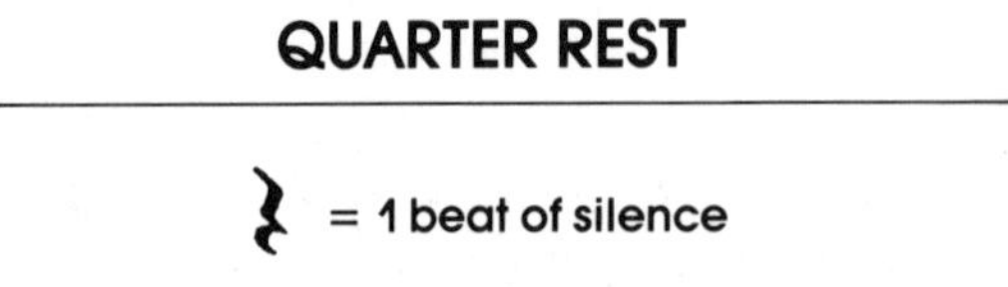

Counting	1	2	3	4
Alternate Counting				

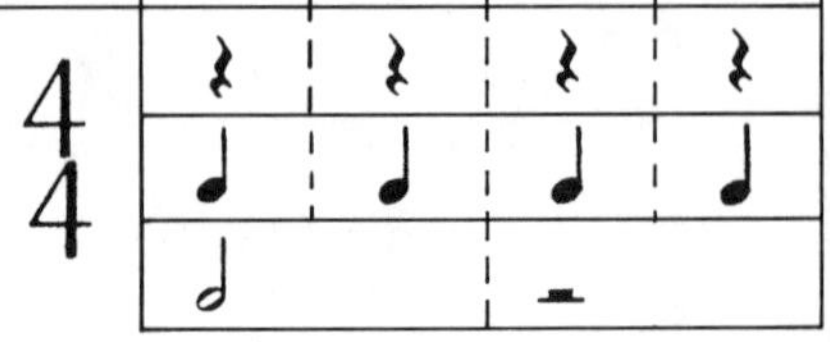

TEACHER: Have all students count aloud as they practice each of the steps listed below. They should learn each line separately before they play it as a duet.

1. Clap and count.
2. Play pizzicato using open D instead of the written pitches.
3. Play arco using open D instead of the written pitches.
4. Play arco or pizzicato as written.

53. COUNTING AND ANSWERS

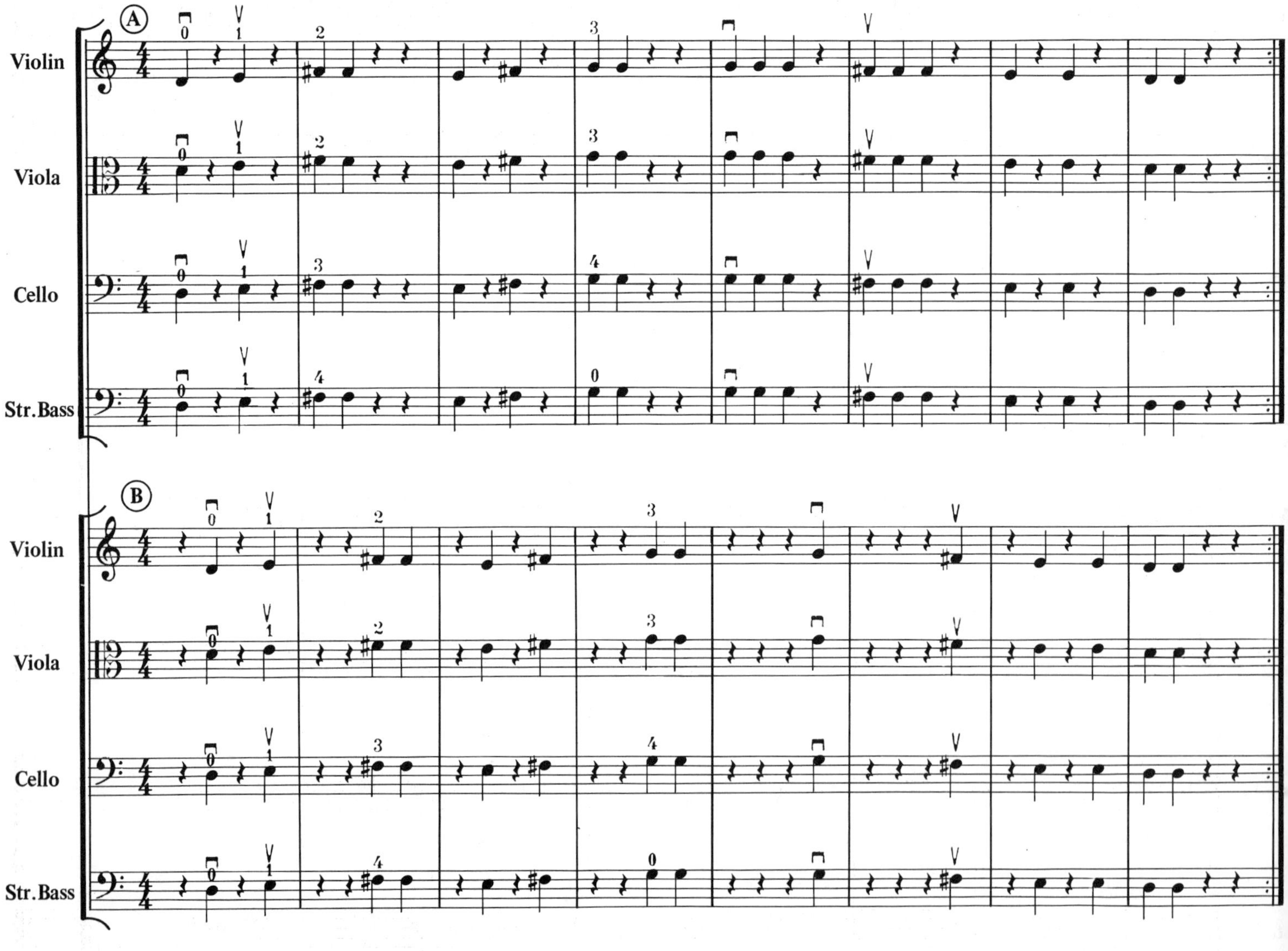

(A)

Violin

Viola

Cello

Str. Bass

(B)

Violin

Viola

Cello

Str. Bass

54. RHYTHM TEASER

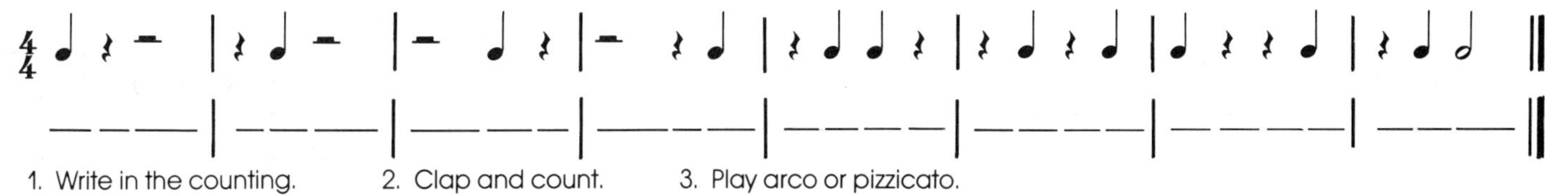

1. Write in the counting. 2. Clap and count. 3. Play arco or pizzicato.

TEACHER: Remind students to prepare their fingers for each skip and to keep fingers down where indicated.

55. SKIPS

TEACHER: Remind students to prepare their fingers for each skip.

56. MORE SKIPS

57. NORWEGIAN FOLK SONG

Traditional

59. RHYTHM TEASER

1. Write in the counting. 2. Clap and count. 3. Play arco or pizzicato.

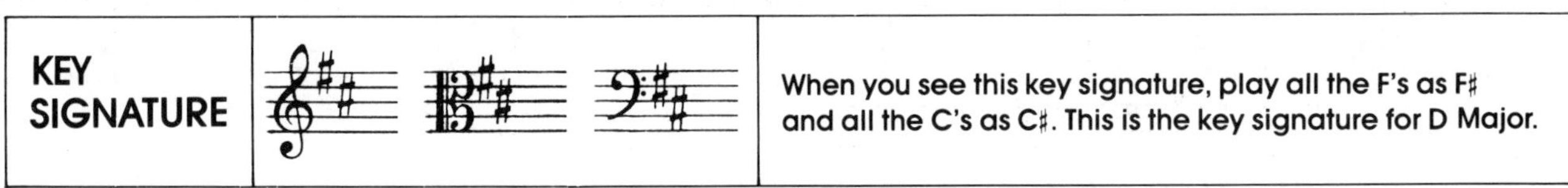

KEY SIGNATURE
When you see this key signature, play all the F's as F♯ and all the C's as C♯. This is the key signature for D Major.

TEACHER: Have the students circle all the notes affected by the key signature.

60.

NEW IDEA

BOW DIVISION	W. B. = Whole Bow U. H. = Upper Half L. H. = Lower Half M. = Middle	W.B. U.H. L.H. M.

TEACHER: Look for opportunities to apply the principles of good bow division with each line. The musical phrasing of each selection will improve through the use of good bow division.

61. BOW DIVISIONS

TEACHER: See score page 25 SEPARATING RIGHT HAND AND LEFT HAND for practice suggestions for Line 62.

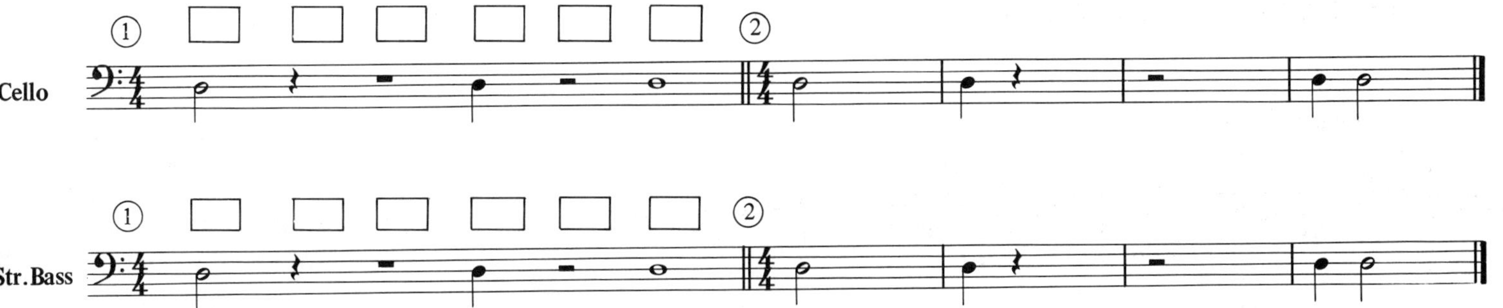

① Write the number of counts each note or rest should receive in each box.
② Complete each measure with the correct number of half notes or quarter notes.

64. JINGLE BELLS

Pierpont

Violin
Viola
Cello
Str. Bass
Piano

L.H. W.B. U.H. W.B.

Vln.
Vla.
Cello
Str. Bass
Piano

★ Check the placement of your bow.

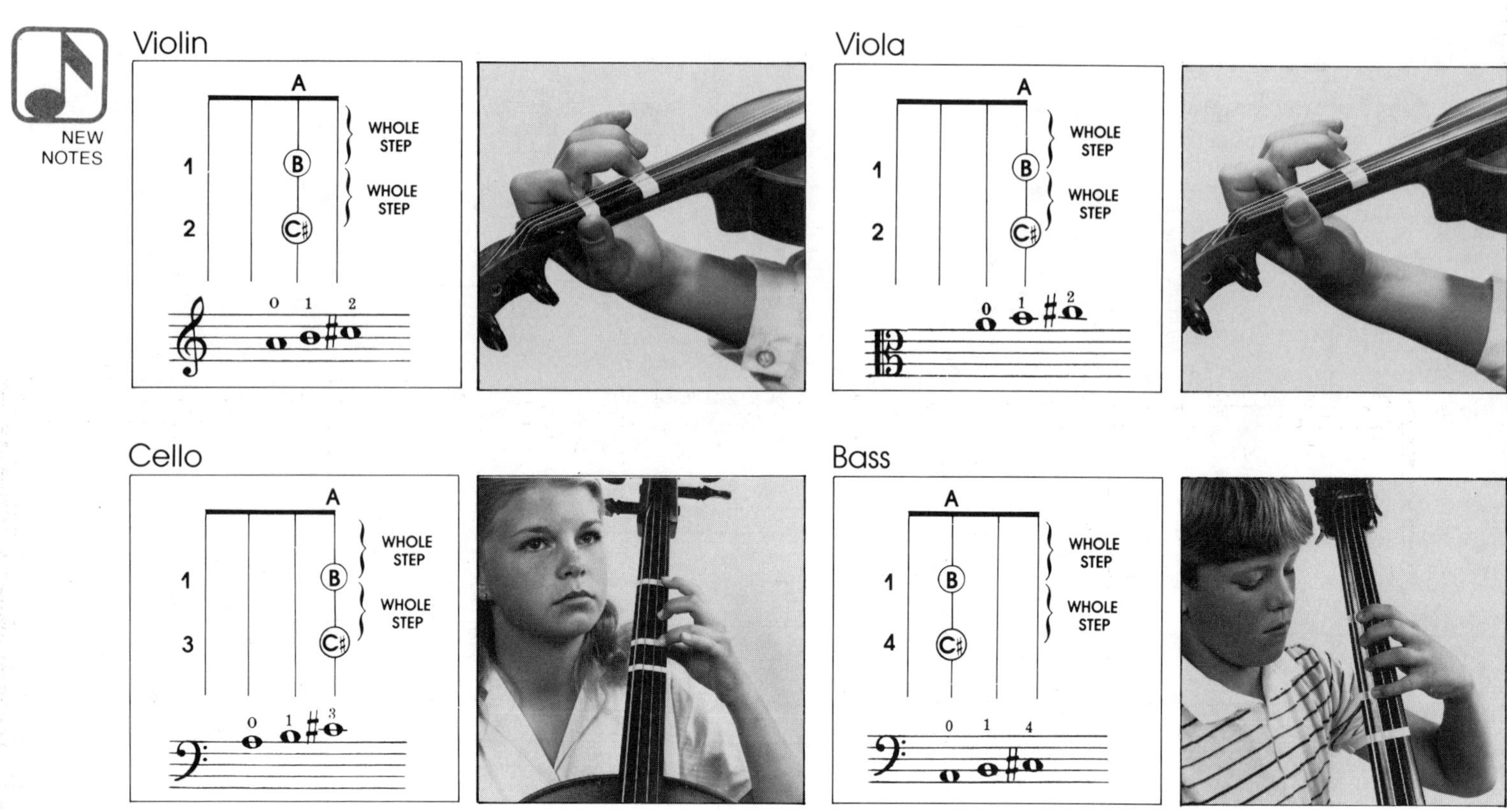

65. NEW NOTES B AND C♯

(A)

Violin

Viola

Cello

Str. Bass

(B)

Violin

Viola

Cello

Str. Bass

66.

TEACHER: This exercise offers an opportunity to stress the relationship of fingers across the strings. Lift and set fingers carefully.

THEORY GAME

67.

★ Write in the note names.

TEACHER: Point out to the students that Line B is the inversion of Line A. Also, students can reverse parts and play the other part on the repeat. This selection makes a good program piece.

68. FRENCH FOLK SONG

Traditional -Duet

TEACHER: Have your students do the Bow Grip Exercises found on student book page 4, score pages 22-23. Students will build the strength and flexibility that is needed for a good bow grip through the constant repetition of these exercises.

TEACHER: This line will require very careful practice to learn each part and to play it as a duet. Have students clap and count each line before playing.

69. LIFT SET GAME

Duet

★ Check your bow grip often.

TEACHER: Check the playing positions of your string players often. Have the students check each other to make them aware of the important points of holding the bow, holding the instrument, posture and bowing. Refer to student book pages 4-5, score pages 14-21.

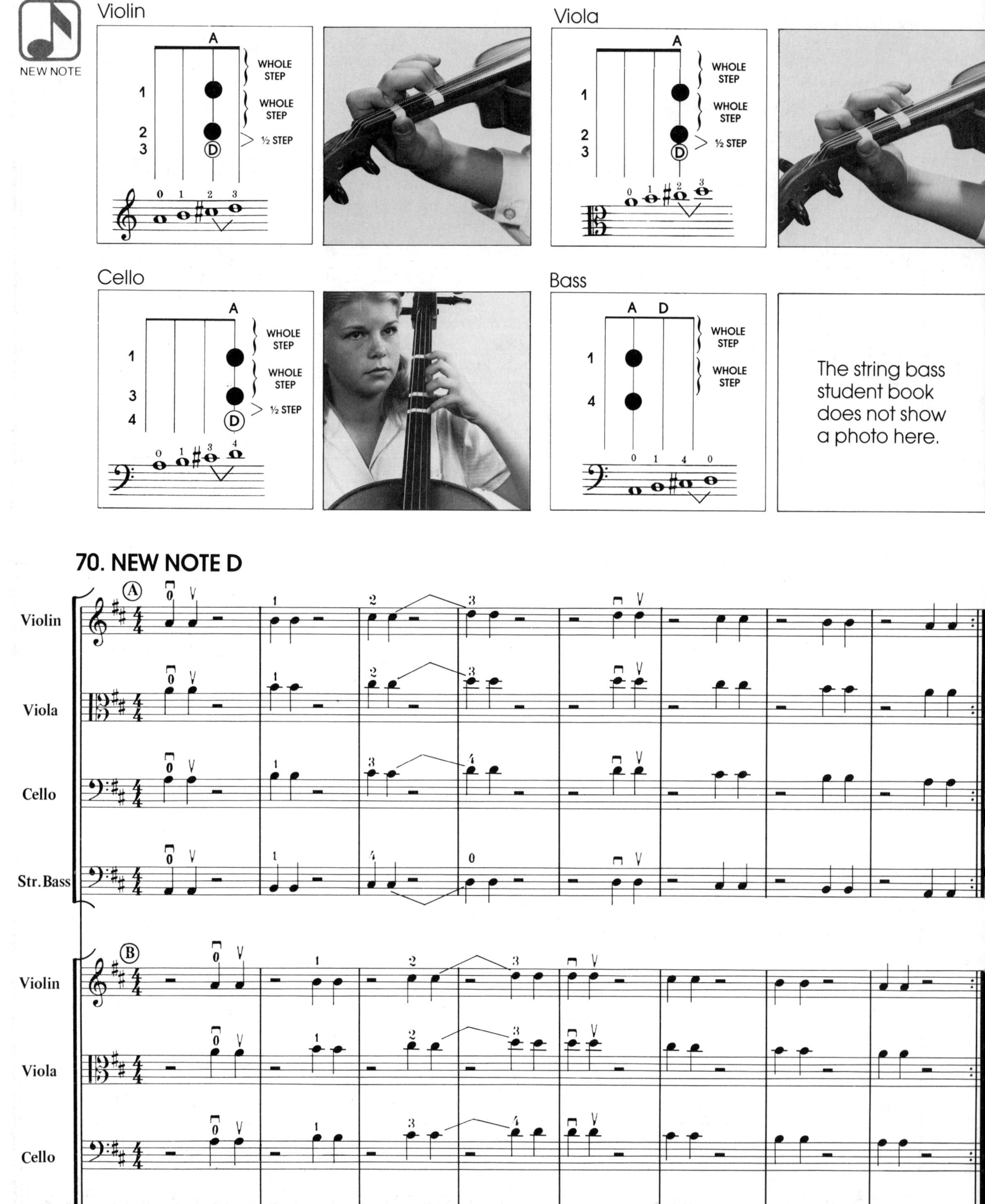
NEW NOTE
Violin
A
WHOLE STEP
WHOLE STEP
½ STEP
1
2
3
D
Viola
A
WHOLE STEP
WHOLE STEP
½ STEP
Cello
A
WHOLE STEP
WHOLE STEP
½ STEP
Bass
A D
WHOLE STEP
WHOLE STEP
The string bass student book does not show a photo here.
70. NEW NOTE D
Violin
Viola
Cello
Str. Bass

TEACHER: Refer to the score and student book inside front cover for an explanation of a tetrachord. Show the students how two tetrachords are combined to form a scale. Use measures 5-6 of Line 72 for an example.

71. TETRACHORD MARCH

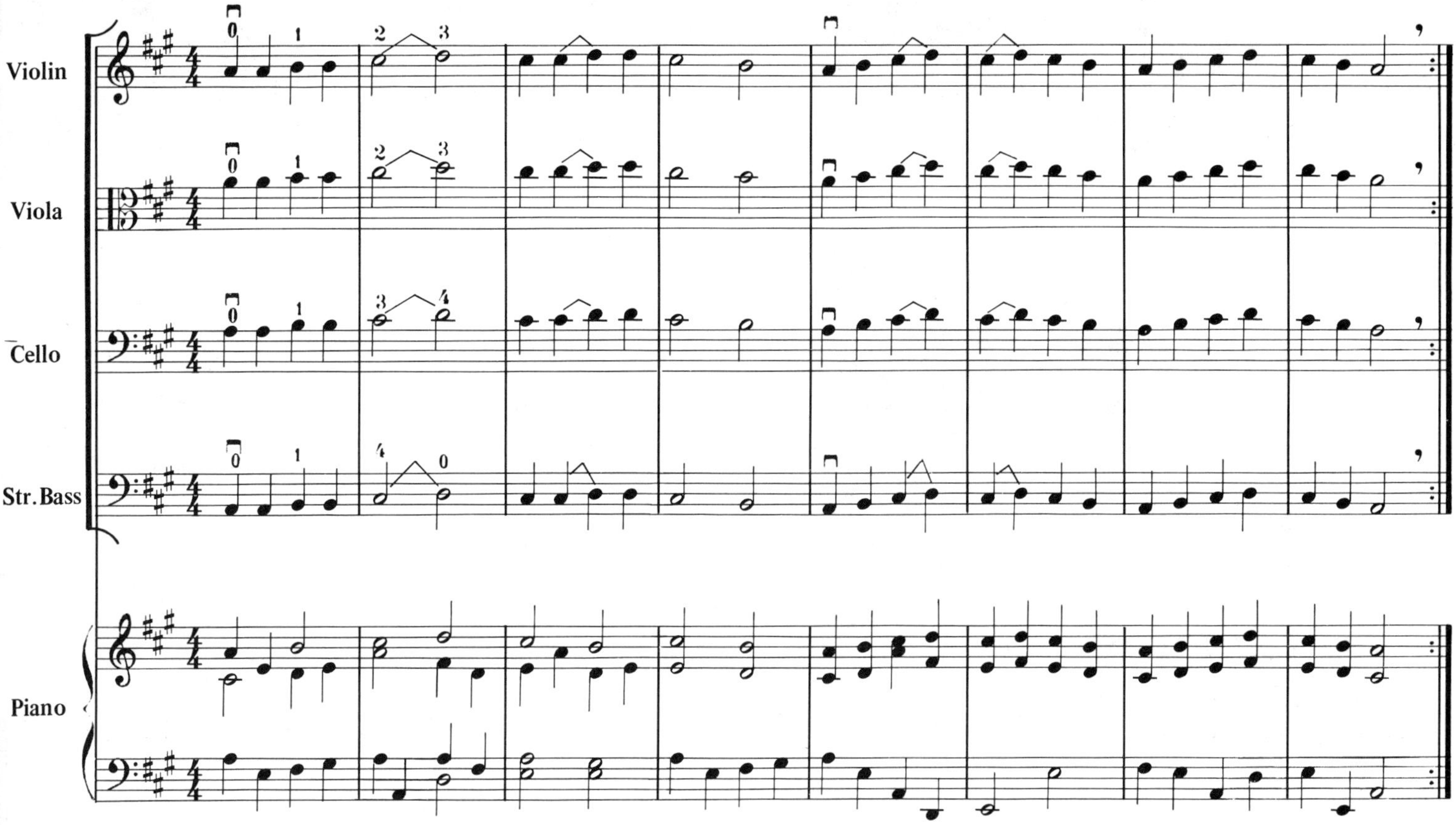

Violin
Viola
Cello
Str. Bass
Piano

★ Refer to the inside front cover for the explanation of a tetrachord.

TEACHER: Refer to student book page 48 for additional technical and developmental material using the D Major scale.

72. UP THE D MAJOR SCALE

Violin
Viola
Cello
Str. Bass

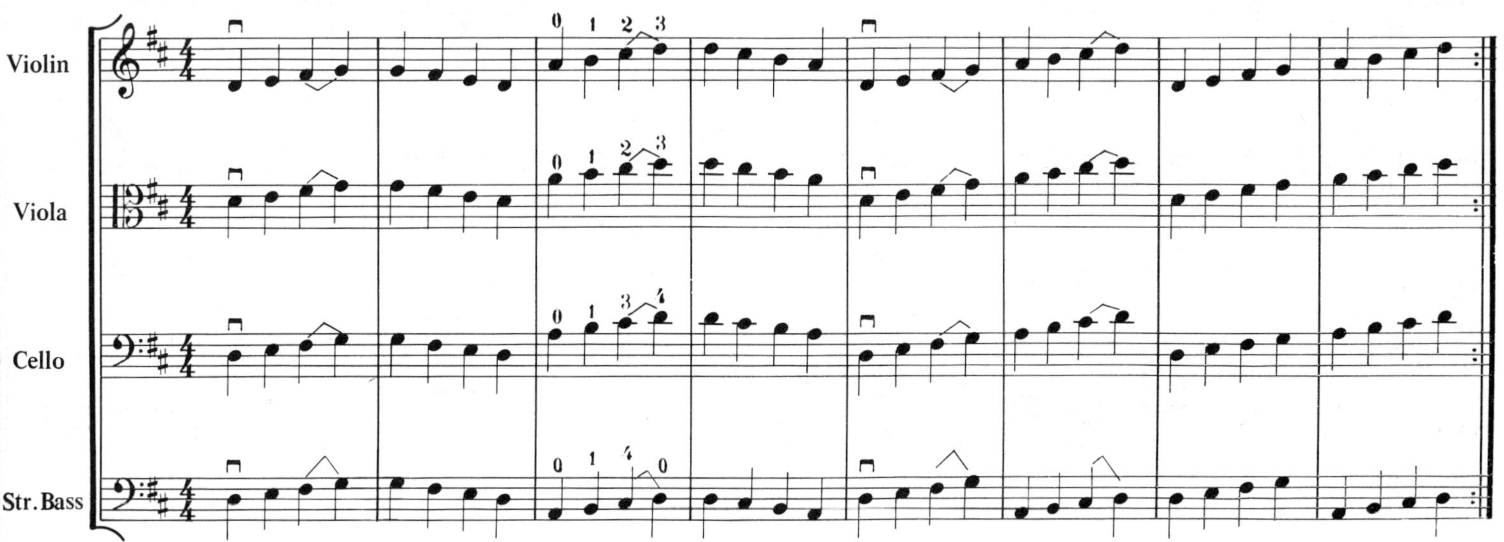

★ Check your left hand position.

TEACHER: Any scale may be played as a two, three or four part round by not repeating the top note.

73. D SCALE ROUND

Round
Violin
Viola
Cello
Str.Bass
I.
II.
III.
★ Prepare the G in measure 6 coming down the scale.
★ Prepare the G in measure 6 coming down the scale.
★ Prepare the G in measure 6 coming down the scale.
1
4

★ Prepare the F# in measure 7 coming down the scale.

TEACHER: These duet rhythms provide a number of possibilities for developing rhythmic independence. They may be played one part at a time or as duets; pizzicato or arco. Additional bowings may be found on student book page 48, score page 174.

74. DUET RHYTHMS FOR THE D MAJOR SCALE

a.

b.

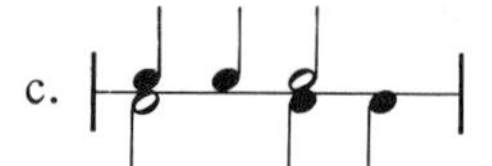
c.

d.

TEACHER: Great strides in bow control and development are possible by young string players using these bowings early in their development. Make a game out of playing more than four notes per bow for both slurred staccato and louré bowings. Use 6-8-12-16 or more notes per bow. Students will enjoy the challenge.

Slurred Staccato
This bowing teaches good bow division, bow control as well as awareness of where the bow is at all times. For example, practicing ♩♩♩♩ teaches a student to play a quarter of a bow for each 𝅝.

Other examples: ♩♩♩ = 𝅗𝅥. ♩♩ = 𝅗𝅥

Louré
The use of arm weight is one of the main factors contributing to a big tone. This bowing teaches how much arm weight can be used before the tone breaks down and becomes scratchy.

NEW IDEA

SLURRED STACCATO BOWING	or Also play 6-8-12-16 notes per bow.	**This bowing is a series of *separated* notes played while the bow moves in one direction. Separate each note from the other.**
LOURÉ BOWING	or Also play 6-8-12-16 notes per bow.	**This bowing is a series of *connected* notes played while the bow moves in one direction. Each note receives a distinct pulse. The bow does not stop but continues moving.**

D.S. AL FINE	*D.S.* (Dal Segno) = sign *Fine* = finish	When you see the *D.S. al Fine*, go back to the 𝄋 (sign) and stop when you come to the *Fine*.

TEACHER: Be sure to explain measure numbers, reinforce good bow division and explain the meaning of the word Ensemble. This piece is an excellent solo to memorize and play with the piano accompaniment.

75. CONCERT SONG

Frost-Solo or Ensemble

Solo

Violin
W.B. U.H. W.B. L.H. W.B.

Viola
W.B. U.H. W.B. L.H. W.B.

Cello
W.B. U.H. W.B. L.H. W.B.

Str. Bass
W.B. U.H. W.B. L.H. W.B.

Ensemble

Violin
W.B. U.H. W.B. L.H. W.B.

Viola
W.B. U.H. W.B. L.H. W.B.

Cello
W.B. U.H. W.B. L.H. W.B.

Str. Bass
W.B. U.H. W.B. L.H. W.B.

Piano

Vln.
Vla.
Cello
Str. Bass
Piano
9
10
11
12
13
14
15
16
Fine

★ Ensemble: A group of musicians playing different parts.

TEACHER: Students must practice these exercises slowly and carefully. Exercises 78 should be played by lifting the finger on one string and setting it down on the next string. These technic trainers are also found later in the book in other keys.

76. TECHNIC TRAINER NO. 1

77. TECHNIC TRAINER NO. 2

★ Roll the bow to the new string.

78. TECHNIC TRAINER NO. 3

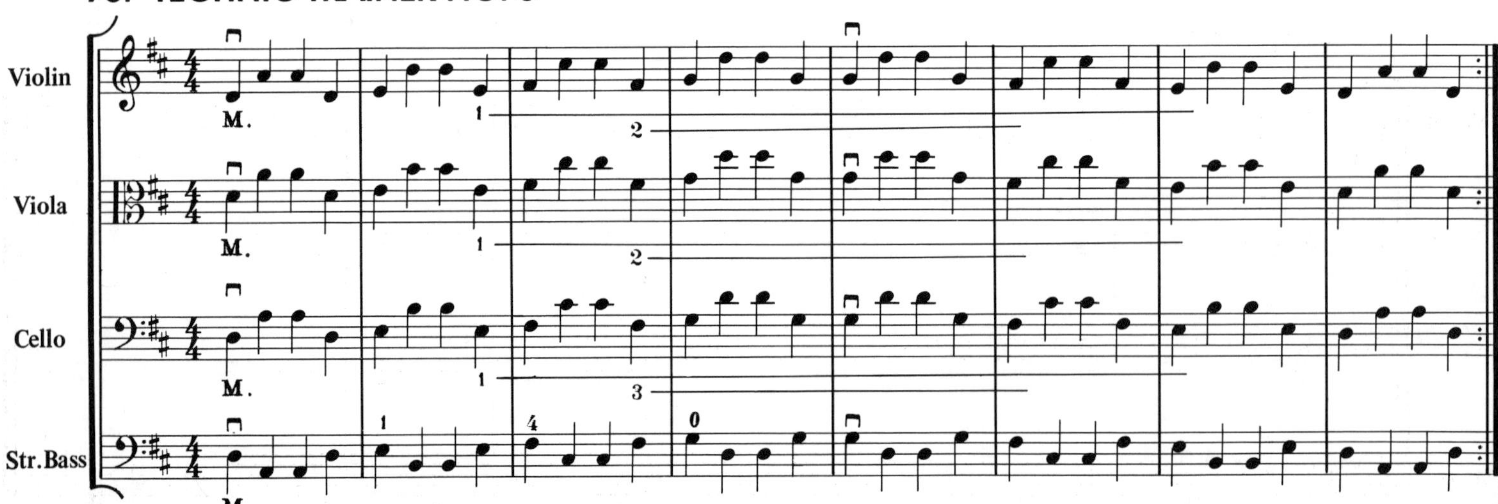

★ Lift and set each finger carefully across to the next string.

TEACHER: You may wish to have the students play Line 79 slurring two quarter notes together after slurs are introduced on student book page 30.

79. TWO OF US

Duet

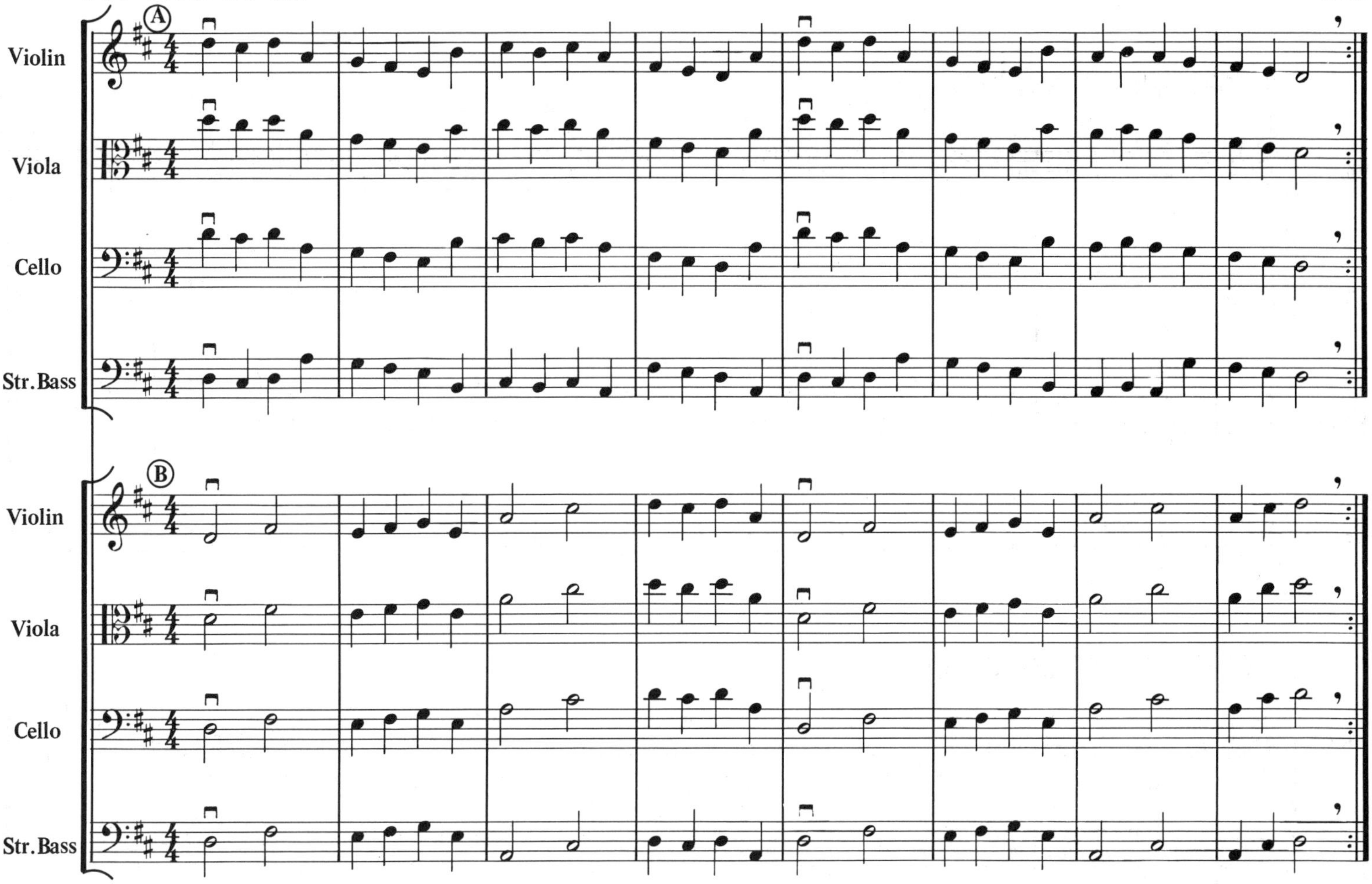

Violin
Viola
Cello
Str. Bass

Ⓐ

Violin
Viola
Cello
Str. Bass

Ⓑ

★ Check your bow grip often.

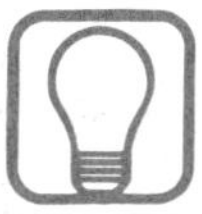

NEW IDEA

WHOLE NOTE
𝅝 = 4 beats

Counting	1	2	3	4
Alternate Counting				
4/4	𝅝			
	𝅗𝅥		𝄼	
	♩	♩	𝄽	𝄽

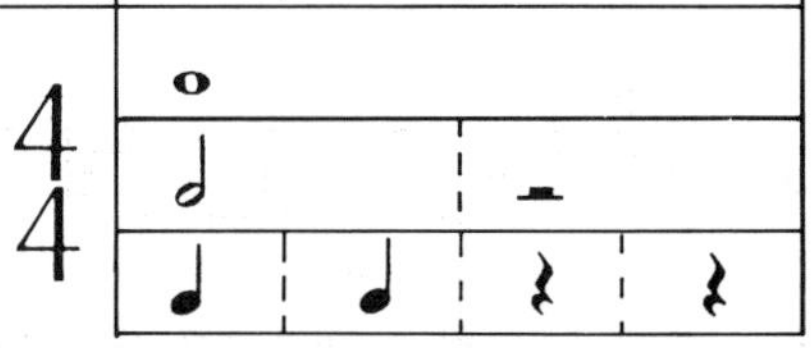

TEACHER: To make students aware that slower bows are needed for whole notes, have them play a whole bow ⊓ bow and V bow for each of the following counts: 1 count, 2 counts, etc. Also play 𝅗𝅥 = ♩♩, 𝅝 = ♩♩♩♩.

80. SLOW BOWS

★ Draw the bow much slower for the 𝅝 (whole) note.

81. BOHEMIAN FOLK SONG

Round

★ Check your left hand position.

AABA FORM	The first musical section A is played two times, followed by a new section B. Then section A is repeated.

TEACHER: This song represents one of the milestones of the beginning stages of development. It offers many opportunities to practice and perfect good bow and finger preparations. Also, there are many well-known variations to go along with this song. It should be memorized and played often.

TEACHER: Stress the value of good bow division to the students and demonstrate the use of a full bow for each 𝅗𝅥 and a half bow for each ♩.

82. TWINKLE, TWINKLE, LITTLE STAR

* Memorize

Mozart

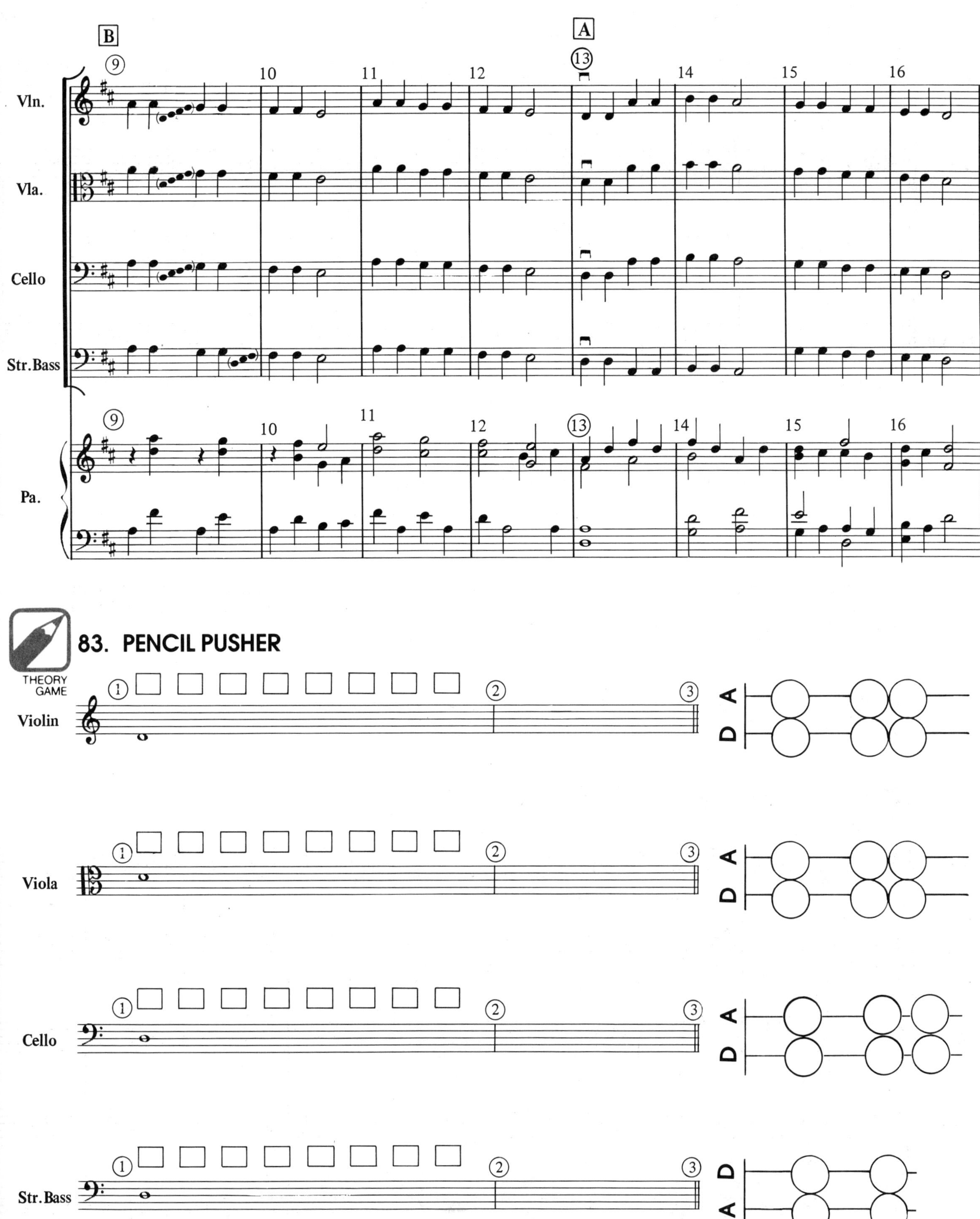

① Draw the notes on the staff to form a D Major scale. Be sure to include the ♯'s for the appropriate notes. Name each note in the boxes above.
② Draw your clef sign. Also add the key signature for D Major.
③ In the fingering chart above, write the name of the note that is played at the place of each circle.

PICK-UP NOTES		Note or notes that come before the first full measure of a piece. Play single pick-up notes up (V) bow.

TEACHER: The pick-up note should be started with the bow placed at the middle using half a bow (lower half). In measures 4, 8, 12: use half a bow (upper half) for the first note, stop the bow at the middle for the rest, use half a bow (lower half) for the note on beat four.
Be sure good bow division is executed for the entire song. This is an excellent song to memorize and play throughout the first year. See score page 25 SEPARATING RIGHT HAND AND LEFT HAND for practice suggestions.

84. O COME, LITTLE CHILDREN

* Memorize

Schultz

Violin — L.H. W.B. U.H. W.B. L.H. U.H. L.H.

Viola — L.H. W.B. U.H. W.B. L.H. U.H. L.H.

Cello — L.H. W.B. U.H. W.B. L.H. U.H. L.H.

Str. Bass — L.H. W.B. U.H. W.B. L.H. U.H. L.H.

Piano

Vln.

Vla.

Cello

Str. Bass

Pa.

TIME SIGNATURE	3/4 = 3 beats in each measure

DOTTED HALF NOTE	𝅗𝅥. 2 + 1 = 3 beats
A dot after a note adds half the value of the note.	

Counting	1	2	3
Alternate Counting			
3/4	𝅗𝅥.		
	♩	♩	♩
	♩	𝅗𝅥	
	𝅗𝅥		♩

TEACHER: Also play this line with the following bowings:

♩♩♩ for each 𝅗𝅥.

♩♩♩ slurred staccato, ♩♩♩ louré

85. D MAJOR SCALE IN 3

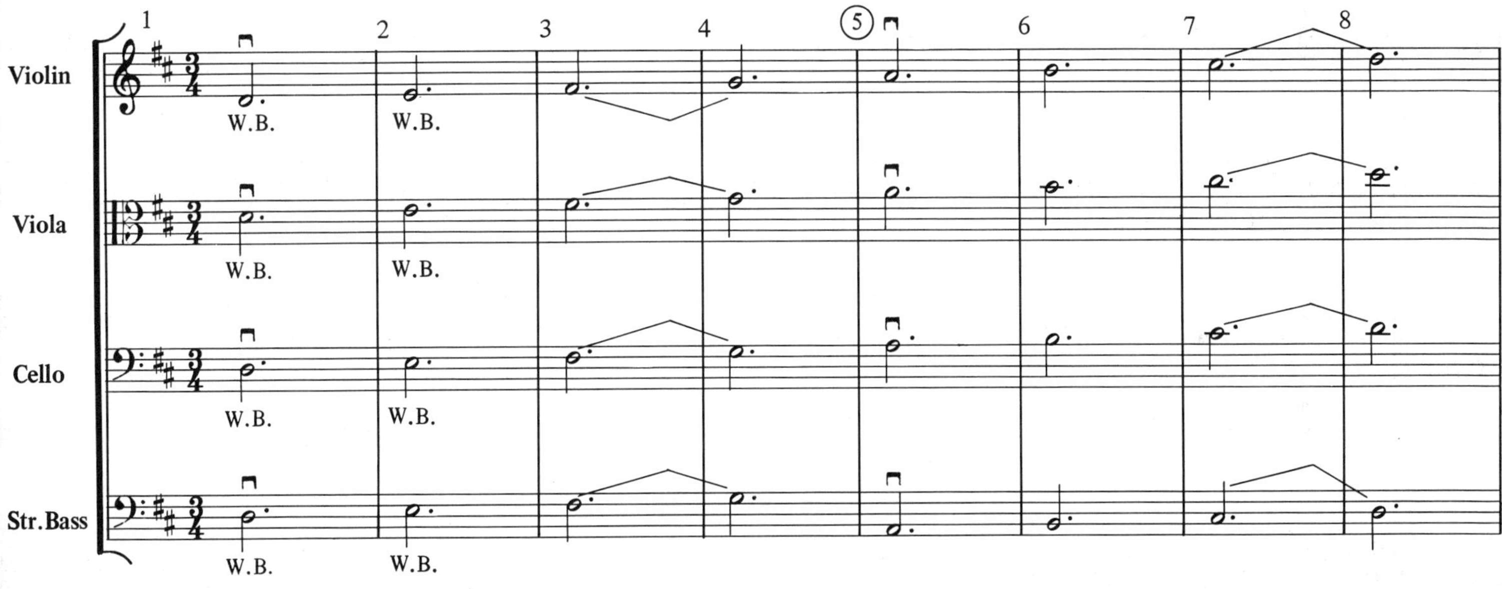

★ Also play this exercise with ♩♩♩ in each measure.

86. D SCALE WALTZ

Violin
L.H. W.B. W.B.

Viola
L.H. W.B. W.B.

Cello
L.H. W.B. W.B.

Str. Bass
L.H. W.B. W.B.

Piano

Vln.

Vla.

Cello

Str. Bass

Pa.

87. RHYTHM TEASER

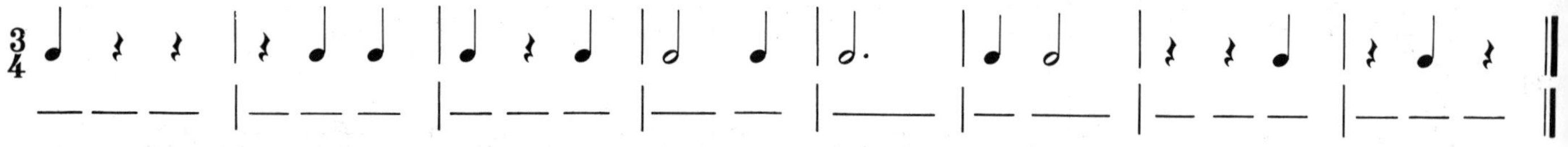

1. Write in the counting. 2. Clap and count. 3. Play arco or pizzicato.

TEACHER: This is an excellent time to check positions. Grades could be assigned or special rewards given to those having the best positions. Use this check list often and have all students refer to it frequently.

88. POSITION CHECK

Violin – Viola

Right Hand	Left Hand	Playing Position
☐ Thumb bent	☐ Wrist straight	☐ Instrument held up
☐ Little finger curved	☐ Elbow under	☐ Sitting up properly
		☐ Straight bow stroke

Have your teacher check your position. Place an X in the box for each item that is correct in your playing.

Cello

Right Hand	Left Hand	Playing Position
☐ Thumb bent	☐ Wrist straight	☐ Instrument up
☐ Little finger over the bow	☐ Elbow up	☐ Sitting up properly
		☐ Straight bow stroke

Have your teacher check your position. Place an X in the box for each item that is correct in your playing.

Bass

Right Hand	Left Hand	Playing Position
☐ Thumb bent	☐ Wrist straight	☐ Instrument tilted in
☐ Little finger over the bow	☐ Elbow up	☐ Standing up properly
		☐ Straight bow stroke

Have your teacher check your position. Place an X in the box for each item that is correct in your playing.

TEACHER: FRENCH FOLK SONG is an excellent song to develop a free flowing bow stroke. Be sure students are in the correct place on the bow (tip) to use a whole bow on the 𝅗𝅥. in measures 4, 8, 12, 16 and 20.

89. FRENCH FOLK SONG

*** Memorize**

Traditional

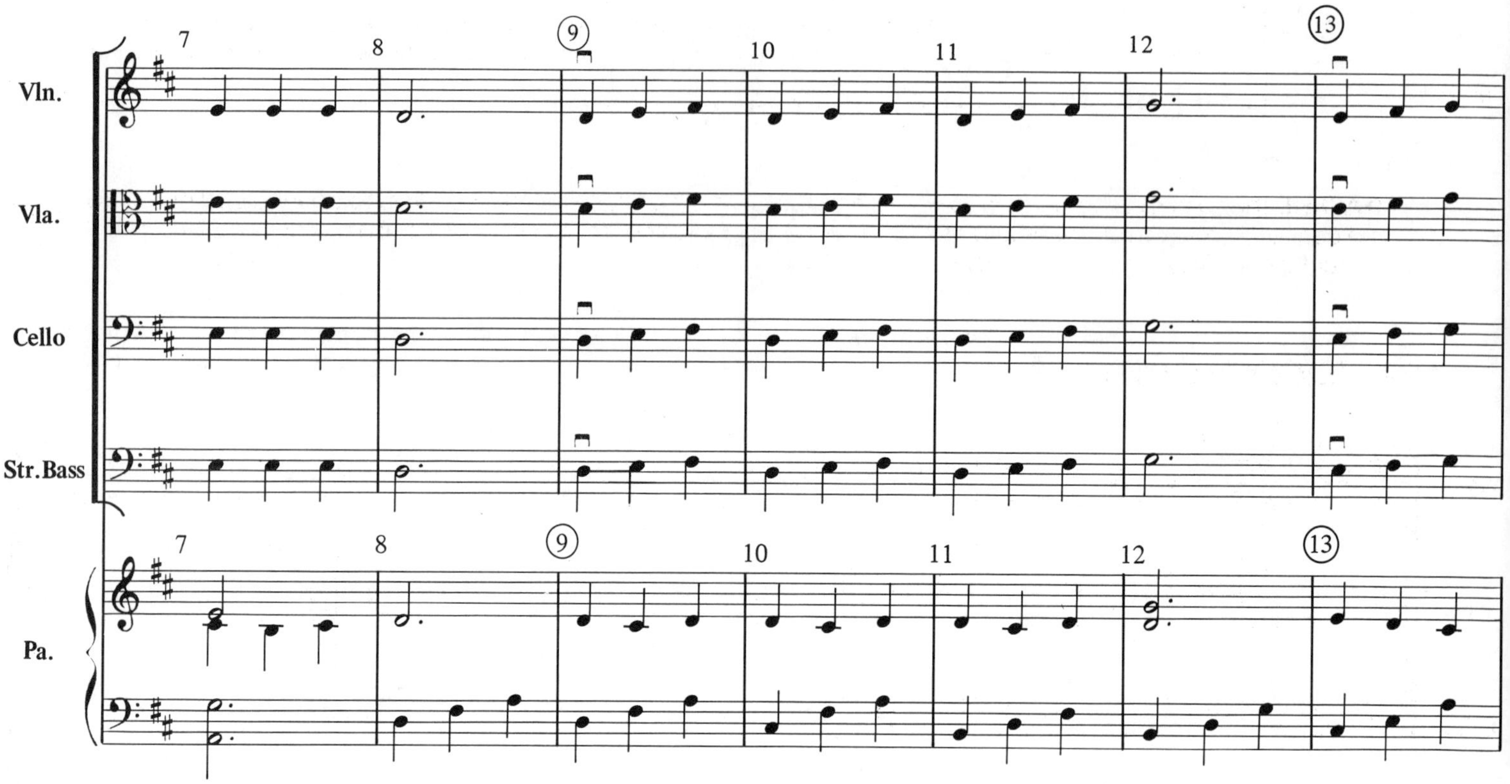

Vln.

Vla.

Cello

Str. Bass

Pa.

7 8 9 10 11 12 13

Vln.

Vla.

Cello

Str. Bass

Pa.

14 15 16 17 18 19 20

90. RHYTHM TEASER

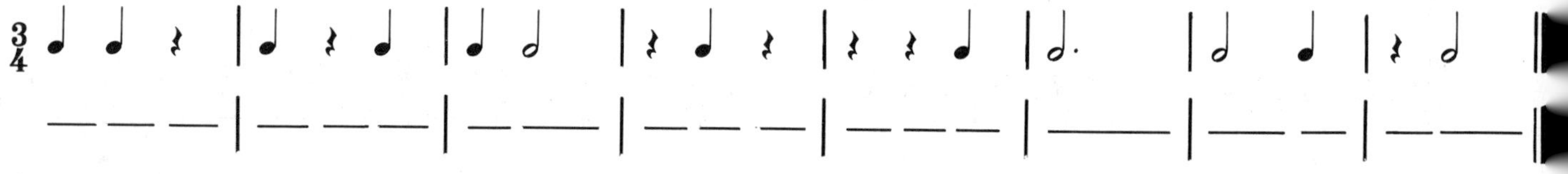

1. Write in the counting. 2. Clap and count. 3. Play arco or pizzicato.

D.C. AL FINE	*D.C.* (Da Capo) = beginning *Fine* = finish	When you see the *D.C. al Fine*, go back to the beginning and stop when you come to the *Fine*.

TEACHER: This is an opportune time to strengthen the counting of rhythms. Ask your class to count aloud and clap the correct rhythm. It may be helpful to write the counting underneath the notes. Students may also say 'rest' at the correct place. There are no bow lifts in this selection.

91. TRICKY MELODY

Violin
Viola
Cello
Str. Bass

★ Clap and count this melody before you play.

Fine

Piano

Vln.
Vla.
Cello
Str. Bass

D.C. al Fine

Pa.

92. SCOTLAND'S BURNING

English Round

93. BALANCE THE SCALE

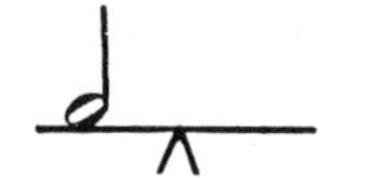

Write in notes or rests to balance each scale. Be sure that the notes or rests on one side of the scale balances with the notes or rests on the other side.

SLUR		**A slur is a curved line that *connects* two or more notes of different pitches. Keep the bow moving and change the fingering for the second note. The sound should be smooth and continuous.**

TEACHER: Slurs may be introduced by having the students play a trill and then slow down the finger motion. Stress that the finger comes straight down on the string and strikes the fingerboard firmly. Slurring two notes in a bow, the bow should be divided equally so that each note sounds for the same length of time.

94.

★ To slur two notes, use half of the bow for each note.

95.

★ Also play this bowing pattern on the A string for exercises 94 and 95.

96.

97.

★ Also play 94 to 97 without slurs.

TEACHER: Slurring across strings creates several types of curves or motions. Put the following diagrams on the chalkboard to help the students understand this important concept.

A. Violin, viola, bass: The curve of the stroke is the same as the curve of the bridge.
Cello: opposite curve.

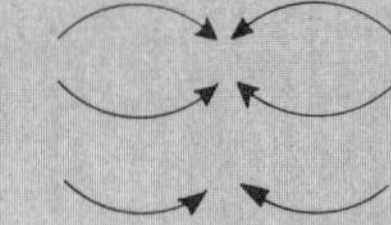

B. Violin, viola, bass: The curve of the stroke is opposite to the curve of the bridge.
Cello: same curve as the bridge.

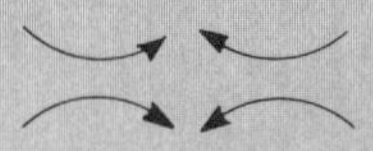

C. Violin, viola, bass: figure 8.
Cello: opposite direction.

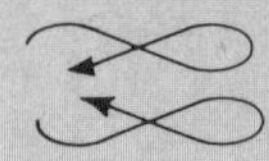

D. Violin, viola: figure 8 (opposite direction from line C).
Cello: opposite direction as violin and viola.
Bass: louré bowing.

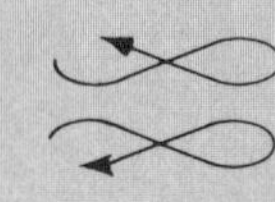

Play each section slowly to accurately learn each type of string crossing. Play each section at least four times.

98. BOW TWISTER

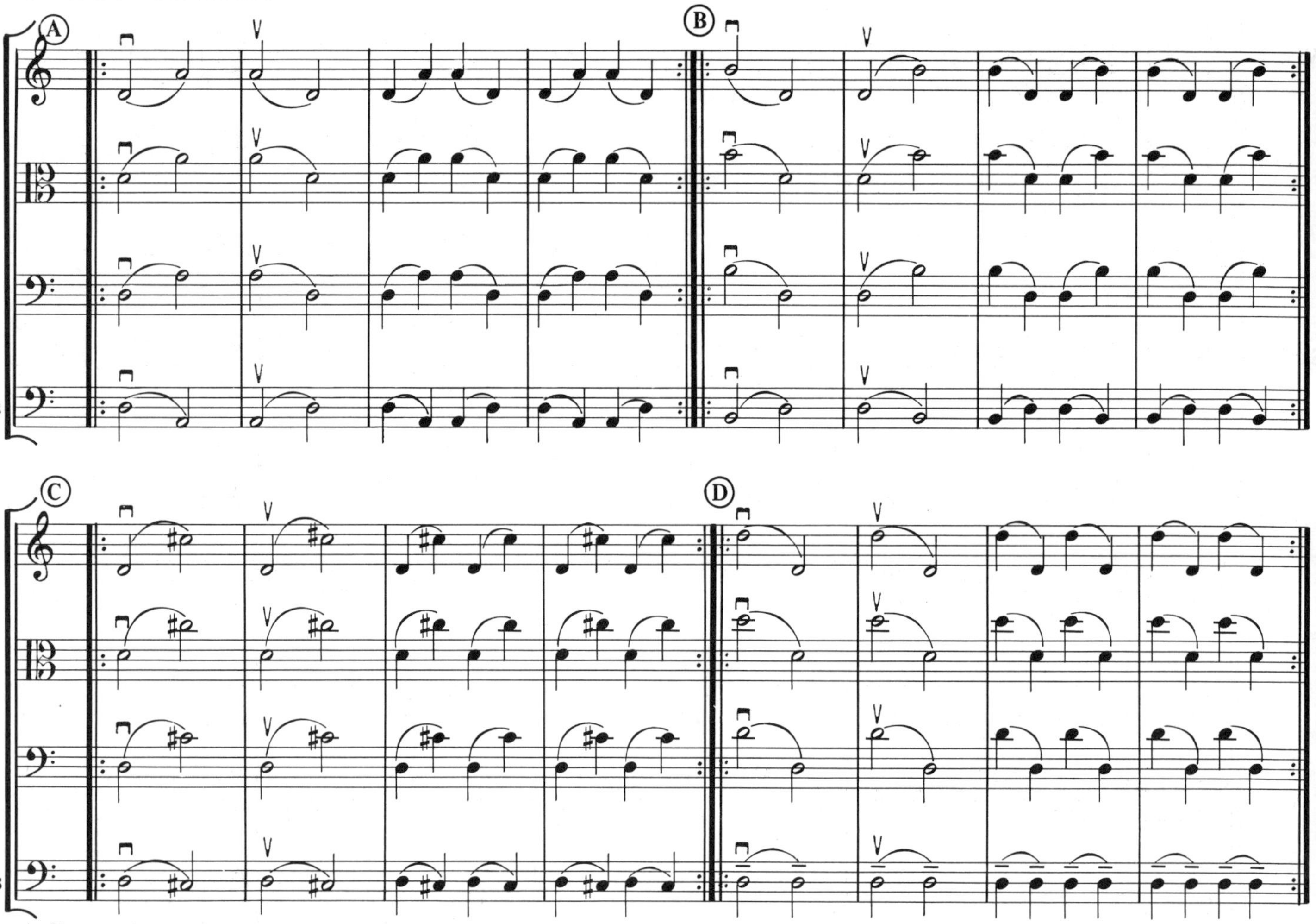

★ Play each section 4 times.

THEORY GAME

99.

★ Write in the note names.

100. GO TELL AUNT RHODIE

* Memorize

American Folk Song

Violin
Viola
Cello
Str. Bass
Piano

W.B. W.B.

Fine

Vln.
Vla.
Cello
Str. Bass
Pa.

D.C. al Fine

78F

TEACHER: This duet can also be played without slurs.

101. IT TAKES TWO

Duet

Responsibility Agreement

musicians' repair & supply

2246 University Ave.
Green Bay, WI 54302-4599

(414) 468-5358 (800) 242-1711
FAX (414) 468-1926

0172

Musicians Repair & Supply herein known as the "Lessor" agrees to lease the equipment described below, and the undersigned Lessee agrees to take the said equipment on a trial lease for a period not to exceed 21 days (through April 3, 1996), with a down payment of $ ——. Within 24 hours of the expiration of the on trial period, the Lessee agrees to return the equipment to the Lessor's business premises. If the equipment is not returned on time, the Lessee agrees to buy the equipment for $1385.00, to be paid in cash within 48 hours of the expiration of the trial period. If Lessee fails to return the instrument on schedule, and fails to buy the equipment, Lessee hereby grants Lessor permission to pick up the instrument wherever it may be stored (including at public or private schools). A pickup charge will be assessed dependent on location and circumstances. Moreover, if the equipment is not returned on time, Lessee agrees to pay a late charge fee of one dollar ($1.00) per day and all costs of collection or repossession, including legal expenses and attorney's fees.

Item & Model	Serial #	Prch Price	Date Retd	Retd Cond
16" Viola 2RR	X7404	$440 —	returned	4-1-96
½ Cello New	A2872	$945.00	returned	4-1-96
— extra rosined bow Cello				

The undersigned warrants and represents that he(she) is over 18 years of age, and that the information stated above is true and correct. Also, the undersigned acknowledges that he/she will be held liable for any loss, damage or late payments, even though another person may be using the equipment. Lessee has read and agrees to conditions stated in this document.

Lessee Signature x Paul Sowinski

Please Print Name Paul Sowinski

Address 8896 Wandering Rd.

City Fish Creek

State/Zip WI, 5422

Phone ( ) 868 - 2246

Soc. Sec. No. ____

Date 3/11/96

Master Card, Visa (No.) ____

(Exp.) ____

Musicians' Repair & Supply [signature]

TEACHER: This line may also be played with slurred staccato bowing: 

102. SLUR THREE

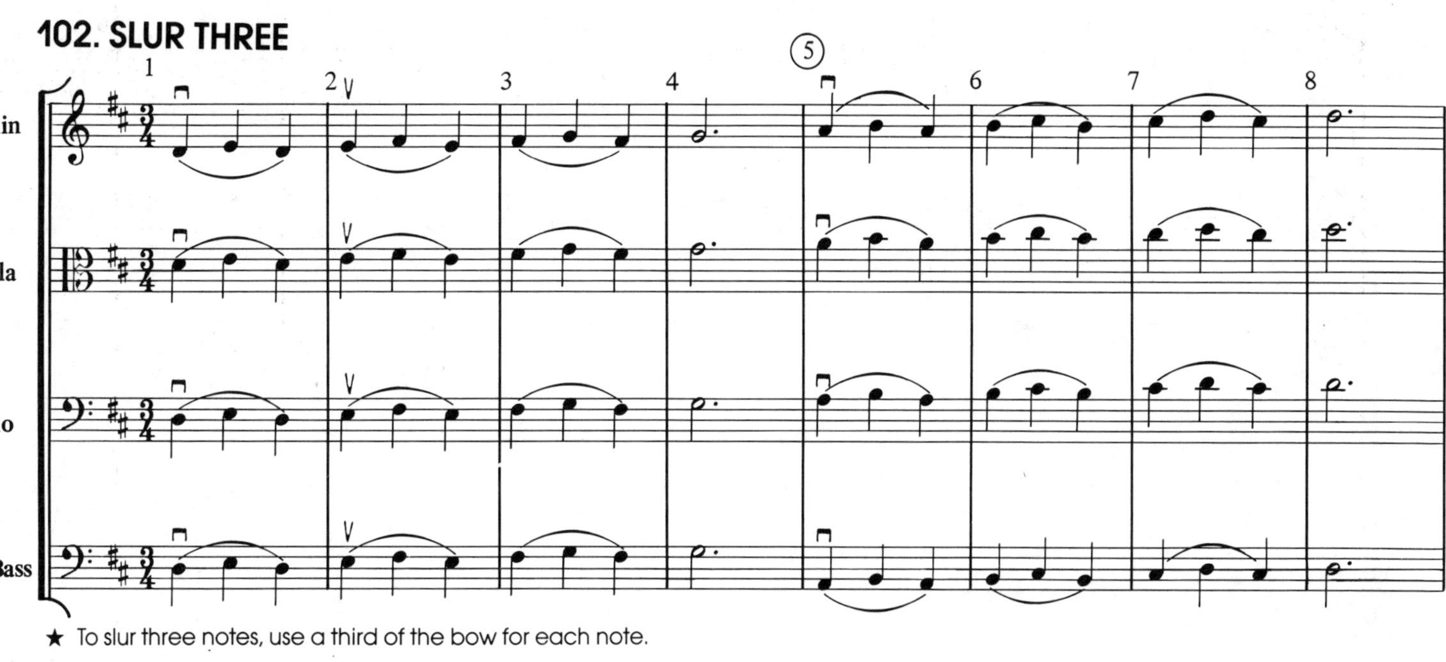

★ To slur three notes, use a third of the bow for each note.

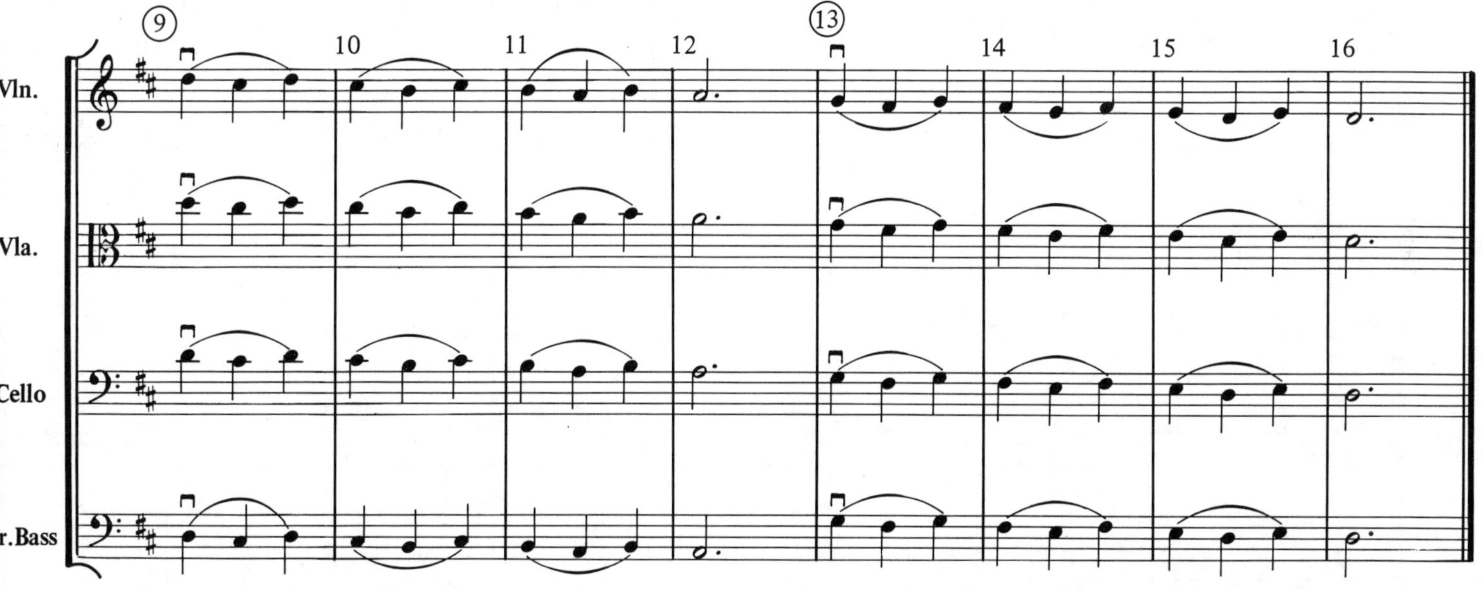

TEACHER: Check the playing positions of your string players often. Have students check each other to make them aware of the important points of holding the bow, holding the instrument, posture and bowing. Refer to student book page 4-5, score pages 14-21. Also see POSITION CHECK, student book page 29, score page 93.

TEACHER: Assign for home practice the Bow Grip Exercises found on student book page 4, score pages 22-23. Students will build the strength and flexibility that is needed for a good bow grip through constant repetition of these exercises.

TIE	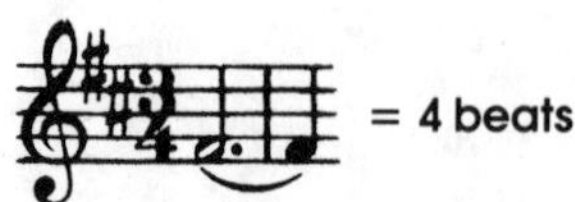 = 4 beats	A tie is a curved line that *connects* two notes of the same pitch. Hold the note for the combined value of the two notes.

103. HICKORY DICKORY DOCK

Traditional

Violin
Viola
Cello
Str. Bass
Piano

Vln.
Vla.
Cello
Str. Bass
Pa.

★ Check your left hand position.

NEW IDEA

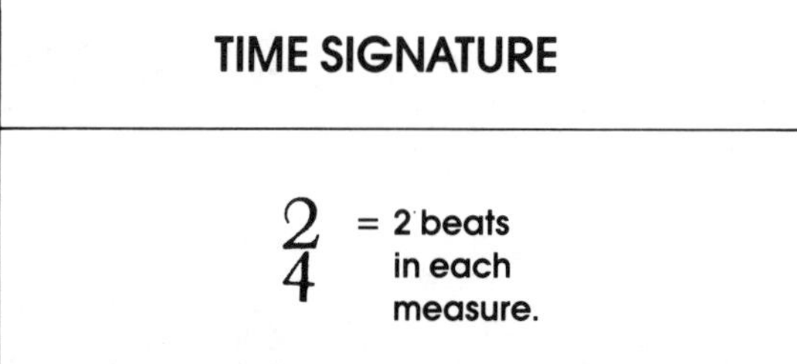
TIME SIGNATURE
2/4 = 2 beats in each measure.

Counting	1	2
Alternate Counting		

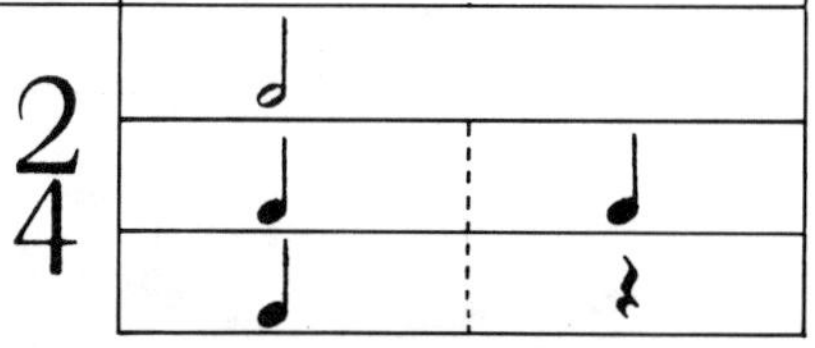

104. TWO STEP MARCH

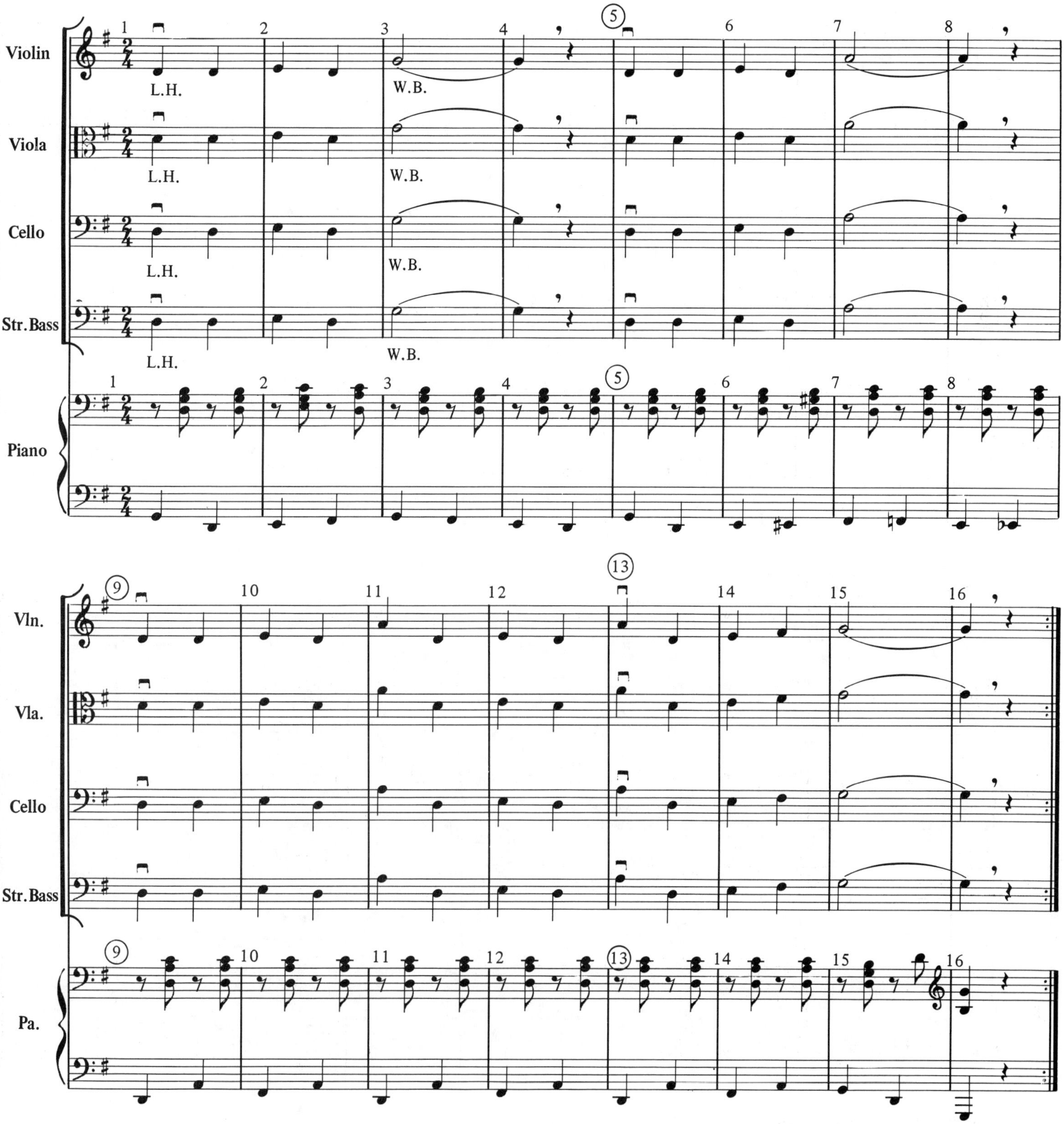

Violin, Viola, Cello, Str. Bass, Piano

L.H.

W.B.

Vln., Vla., Cello, Str. Bass, Pa.

★ Check your bow grip often.

NEW IDEA

ARPEGGIO	**An arpeggio is a broken chord. The notes of the chord are played one at a time.**

TEACHER: Help the violin and viola students to recognize the placement of fingers across the strings. The 3rd finger D on the A string is only a half step away from the 2nd finger F♯. Good intonation is developed as students recognize finger relationships and spacings on each string and across strings.

105. D ARPEGGIO

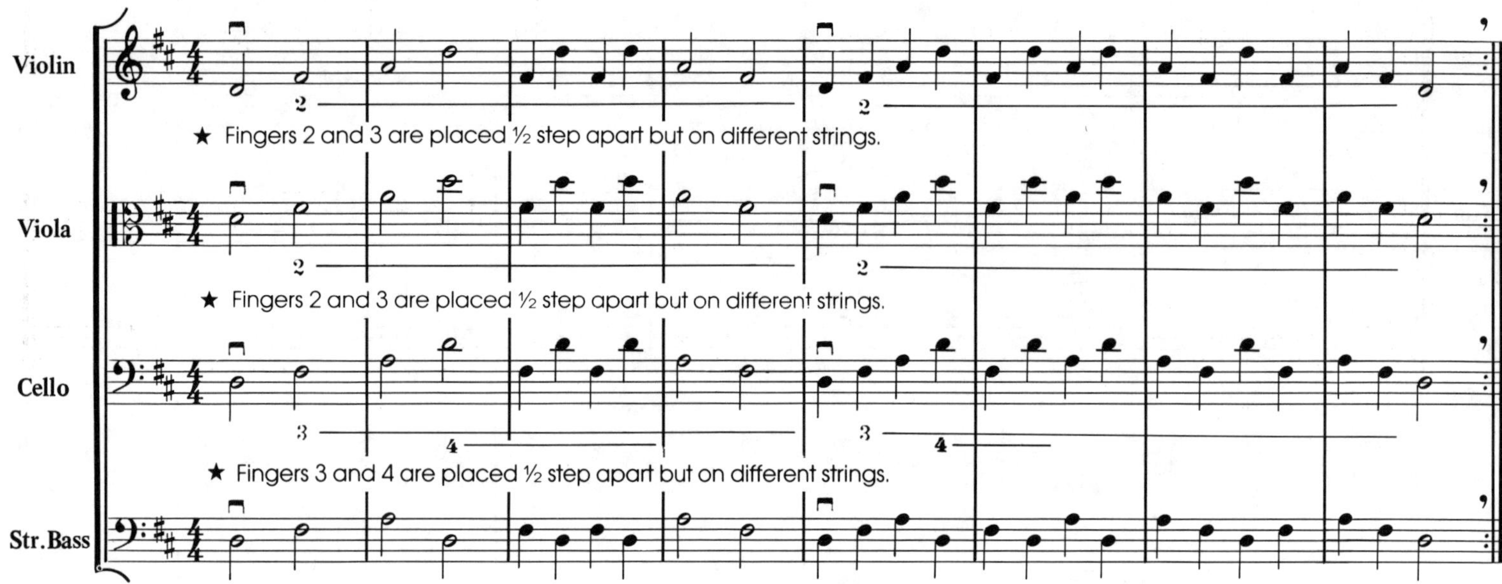
Violin
★ Fingers 2 and 3 are placed ½ step apart but on different strings.
Viola
★ Fingers 2 and 3 are placed ½ step apart but on different strings.
Cello
★ Fingers 3 and 4 are placed ½ step apart but on different strings.
Str.Bass

★ Fingers 4 and 1 are placed 1 step apart but on different strings.

106. ARPEGGIO MARCH

Violin
Viola
Cello
Str.Bass
Piano

Vln. Vla. Cello Str. Bass Pa.

9 10 11 12 13 14 15 16

★ Check the placement of your bow.

107. THE GUIDING HAND

Hatton

Violin Viola Cello Str. Bass Piano

1 2 3 4 5 6 7 8

★ Check your bow grip often.

TEACHER: SOLO TIME may be performed as an individual solo or as a group solo. Prepare for slurred measures by working towards the tip or the frog of the bow because a full bow needs to be used for each slur. It is also important to control the bow speed during the slur so that a third of a bow is used for each quarter note.

108. SOLO TIME

Frost

THEORY GAME

109. PENCIL PUSHER

★ Draw in the bar lines for each section. Be sure to notice the time signatures.

Violin

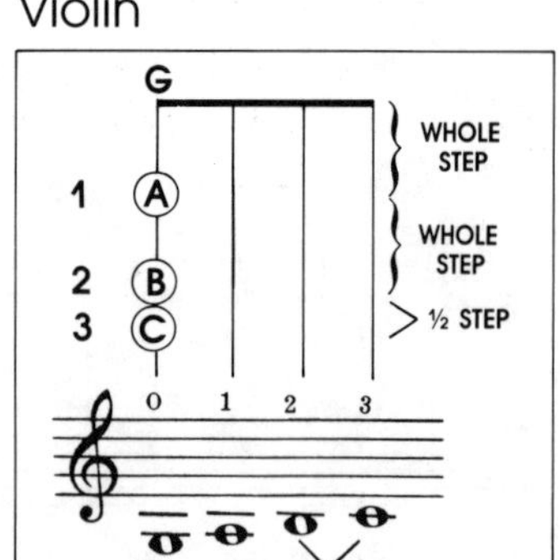

Viola

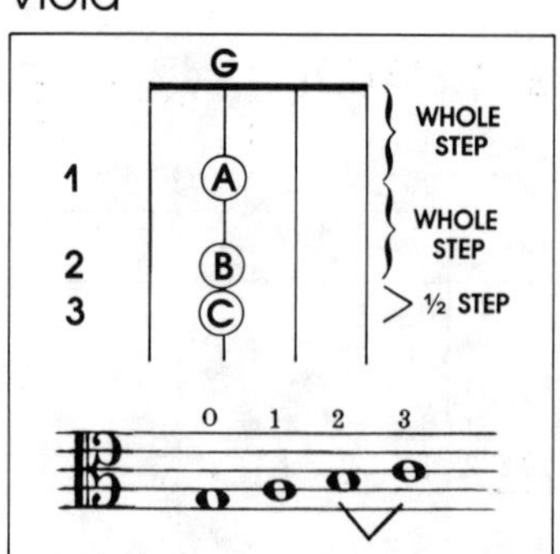

Cello

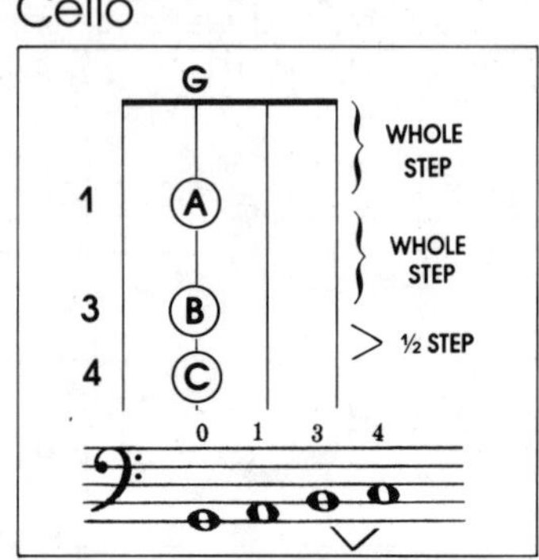

Bass

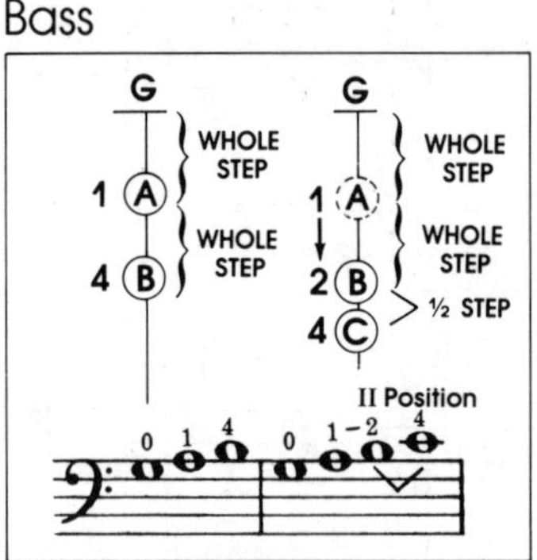

TEACHER: You will need to remind your violin and bass students about ledger lines.

TEACHER: Shifting to 2nd position is introduced to the bassists at this time. You may want to explain and demonstrate shifting to the entire class, however, the other instruments will not use shifting until a later book. Shifting to play in higher positions will allow string players to extend the playing range on their instruments. Use the following shifting hints for the bass players for Line 111:

1. Shift on the 1st finger and move the hand ½ step down the instrument and then place the 2nd finger firmly.
2. Shift back to 1st position sliding the 1st and 2nd finger a ½ step and then lift the 2nd finger.
3. Stress the importance of the ENTIRE hand moving as a unit.
4. The thumb should always be kept behind the 2nd finger.
5. It is important for the students to hear the note to which they are moving.
6. Practice the following study to achieve good intonation on the shift:
   Play A to B; 1 to 4, then A to B; 1 to 2 (2nd position).

110.

111.

★ Ask your teacher to show you how to shift up to 2nd position and back to 1st position.

★ The dash (-) indicates a shift to a new position.

When you see this key signature, play all the F's as F♯. This is the key signature for G Major.

112. NEW NOTES A, B AND C

Ⓐ

Ⓑ

113.

★ Be sure to prepare your fingers for the skips.

114.

Violin
Viola
Cello
Str. Bass

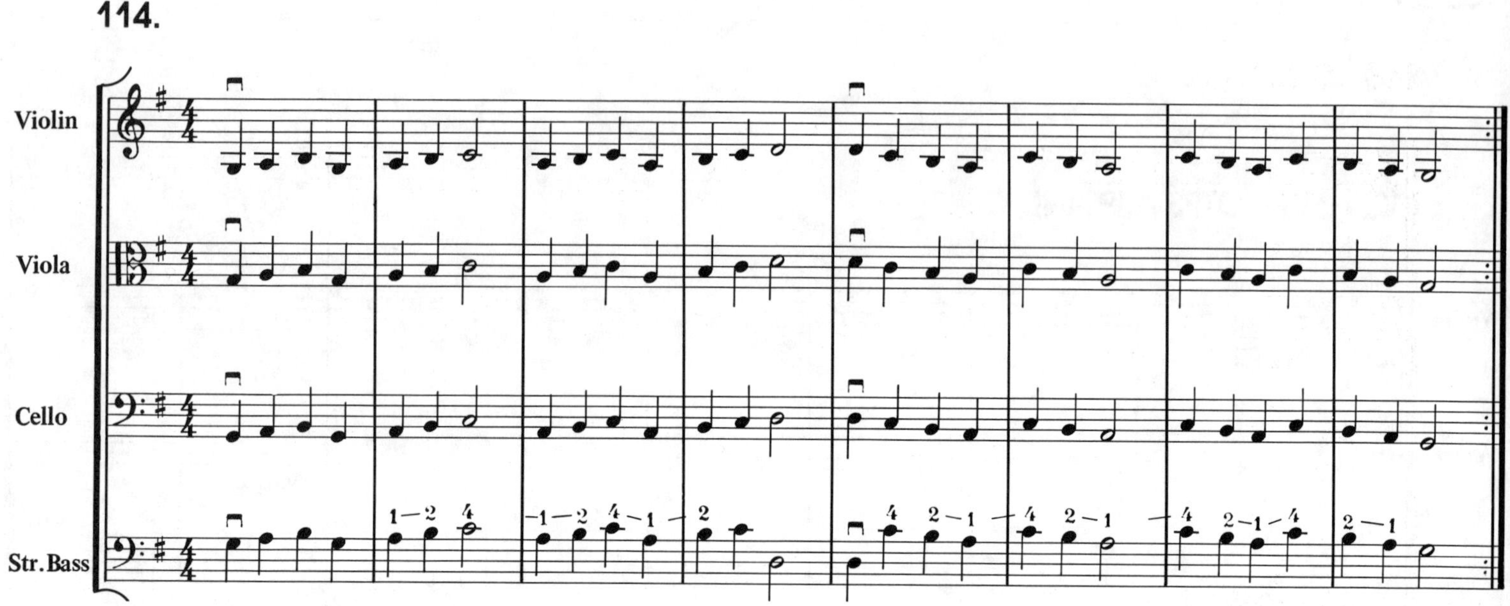

★ Keep your fingers down where possible.

115. LONDON BRIDGE

Traditional

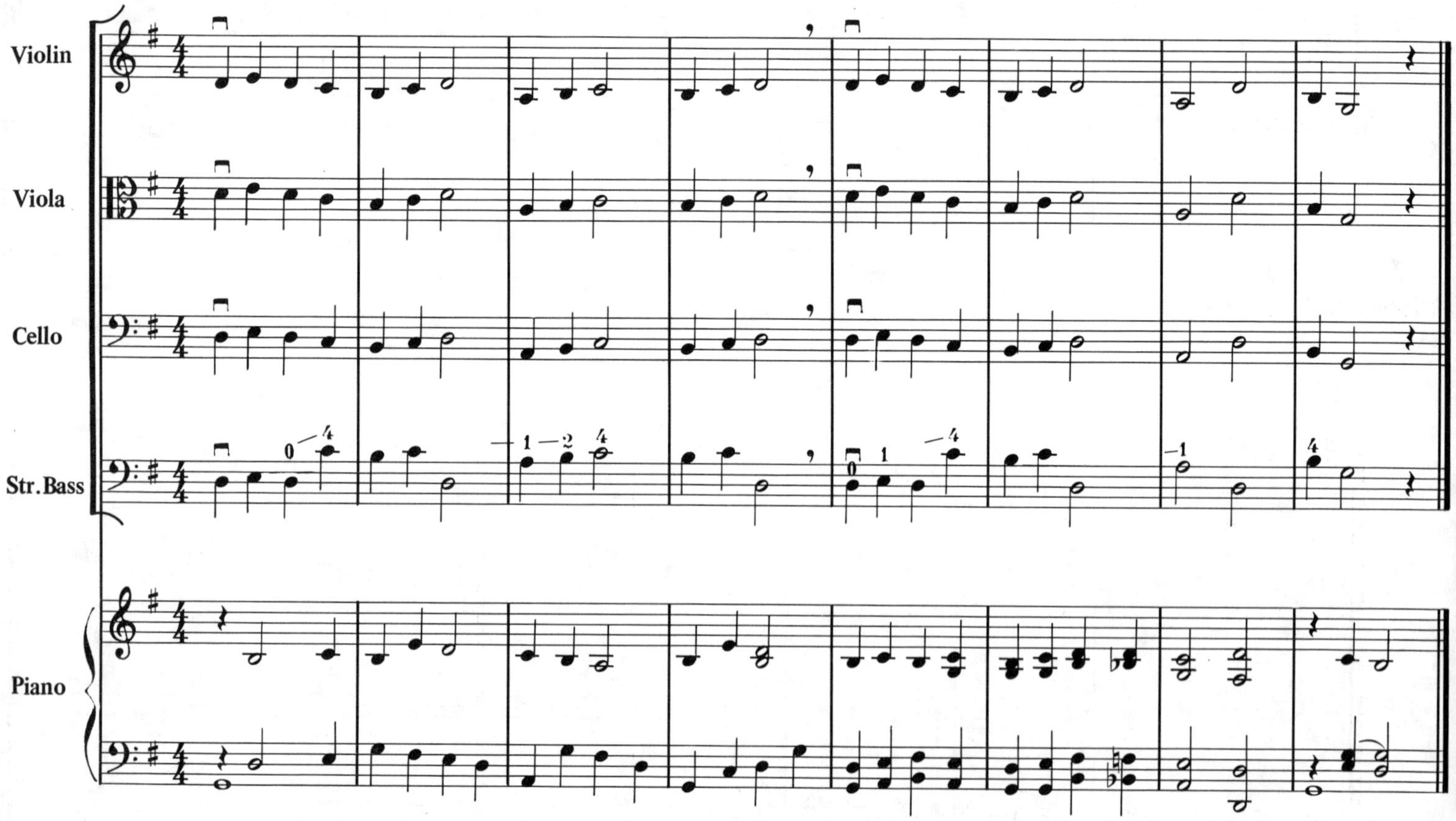

Violin
Viola
Cello
Str. Bass
Piano

★ Check your left hand position.

TEACHER: Check for student knowledge of the G Major scale by having them spell each scale step by letter also indicating the placement of the half steps. Bow division should be carefully checked. Refer to student book page 48, score page 173 for additional technical and developmental material using the G Major scale.

116. G MAJOR SCALE

1 2 3 4 (5) 6 7 8

Violin
W.B. U.H. W.B. L.H.

Viola
W.B. U.H. W.B. L.H.

Cello
W.B. U.H. W.B. L.H.

Str. Bass
II Pos. –2 4 0 1 II Pos. –2 4
W.B. U.H. W.B. L.H.

(9) 10 11 12 (13) 14 15 16

Vln.

Vla.

Cello

Str. Bass
II Pos. 4 2 –1 II Pos. –4 2 –1 0

★ Refer to page 48 for other bowing and scale possibilities.

STUDENT BOOK—Page 34

117.

118. TECHNIC TRAINER NO. 1

TEACHER: Remind the students to lift the finger from one string, place it across on the next string and back again. Do not let them roll or flatten the finger to play the note across the string. Practicing this technique faithfully will develop finger strength and independence. Be sure students leave fingers down where indicated.

119. TECHNIC TRAINER NO. 2

TEACHER: Reinforce to students that in playing skips (thirds) it is important to leave fingers down where possible and to place all fingers down that are part of the skip. If necessary, play the notes between the skip or preparation notes to achieve good intonation.

120. TECHNIC TRAINER NO. 3

★ Special challenge. Play this line with the following bowing: 

TONIC	The tonic is the keytone or first note of a scale. It is shown by I.
DOMINANT	The dominant is the fifth note of a scale. It is shown by V.

TEACHER: Explain to the class that arpeggios are notes of a chord played one at a time. Tonic arpeggios are notes of a chord built on the first note of a scale. Dominant arpeggios are notes of a chord built on the fifth note of a scale.

121. TONIC AND DOMINANT ARPEGGIOS

122. PETER PETER

Traditional

123. REUBEN AND RACHEL

American Folk Song

TEACHER: This is a good time to explain the use of accidentals. Be sure to show that accidentals last for only one measure. In MELODY FOR THREE STRINGS, the C♯ is added in measure 9 because the tonality has moved to D Major. C♮ is played in measure 14 because the tonality has moved back to G Major.

124. MELODY FOR THREE STRINGS

Vln.
Vla.
Cello
Str. Bass
Pa.
9 10 11 12 13 14 15 16
9 10 11 12 13 14 14 16

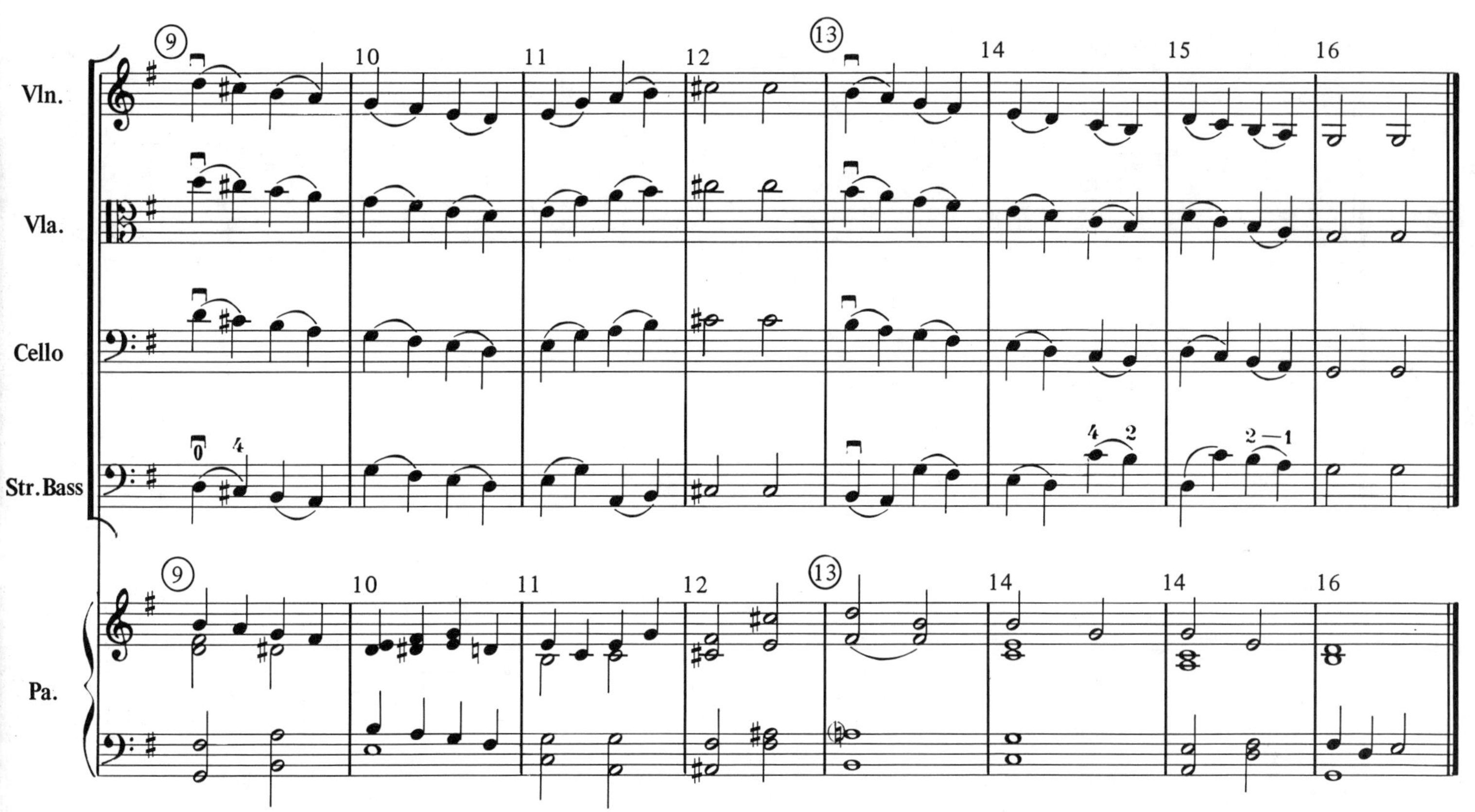

★ Be sure to notice the accidental (♯) in measures 9 and 12.

STUDENT BOOK—Page 35

125. THREE STRING MADNESS

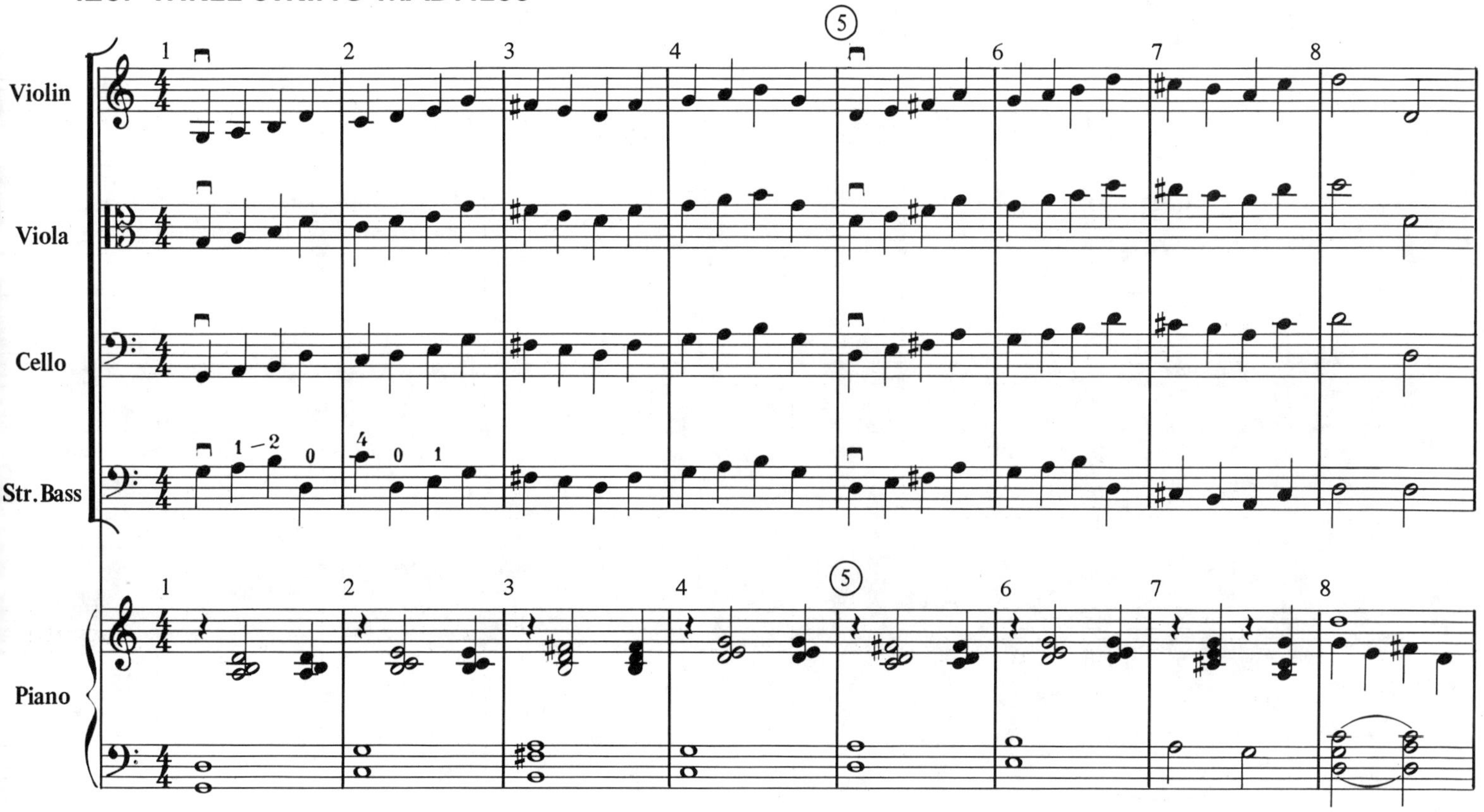

Violin
Viola
Cello
Str. Bass
Piano
1 2 3 4 5 6 7 8

Vln. Vla. Cello Str. Bass Pa.

9 10 11 12 13 14 15 16

★ Special challenge. Play lines 124 and 125 with the following bowings:

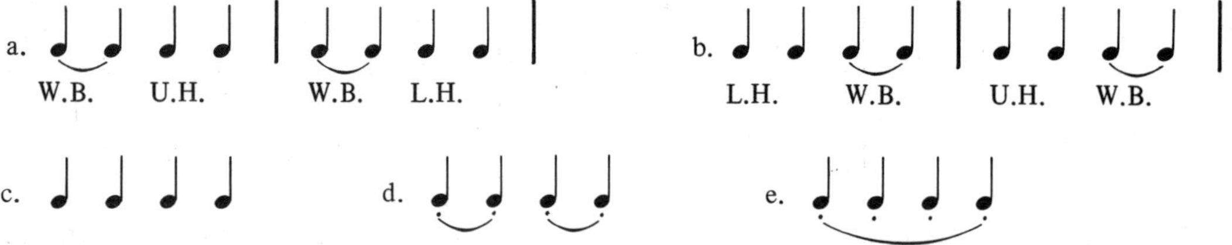

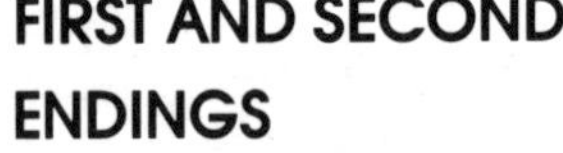 FIRST AND SECOND ENDINGS	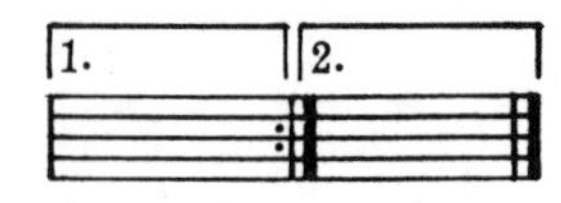	Play the first ending the first time. Then repeat the same music, skip the first ending, and play the second ending.

TEACHER: CONCERT TRIO will work well as a solo, duet or trio and will work well with any combinations of instruments. This selection offers a good review of the A, D and G strings. Listed are some bowing and rhythm variations possible with this selection.

126. CONCERT TRIO

Frost-Trio

Vln.
Vla.
Cello
Str. Bass
Pa.
D.C. al Fine

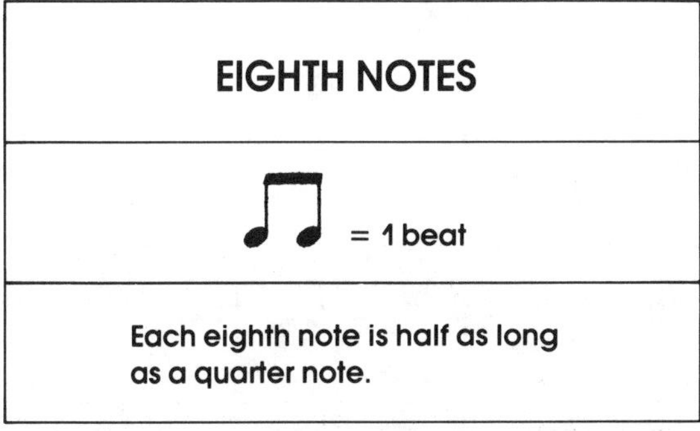

EIGHTH NOTES
= 1 beat
Each eighth note is half as long as a quarter note.

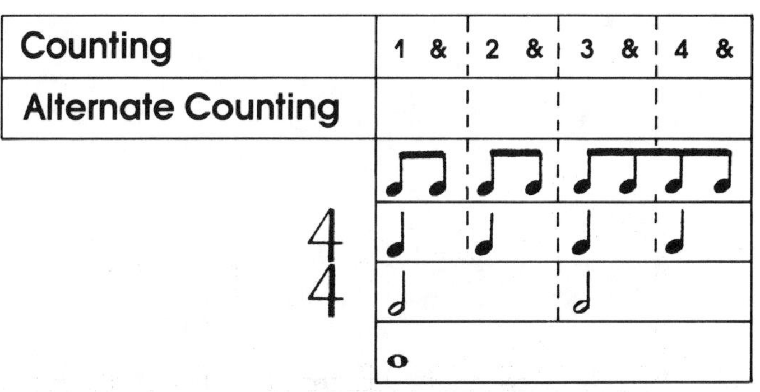

TEACHER: Have the students play these eighth notes at the middle, tip and frog. Additional bowing rhythms and variations can be found on student book page 48, score page 174. Be sure proper bow division is used for these additional rhythms and variations.

127.

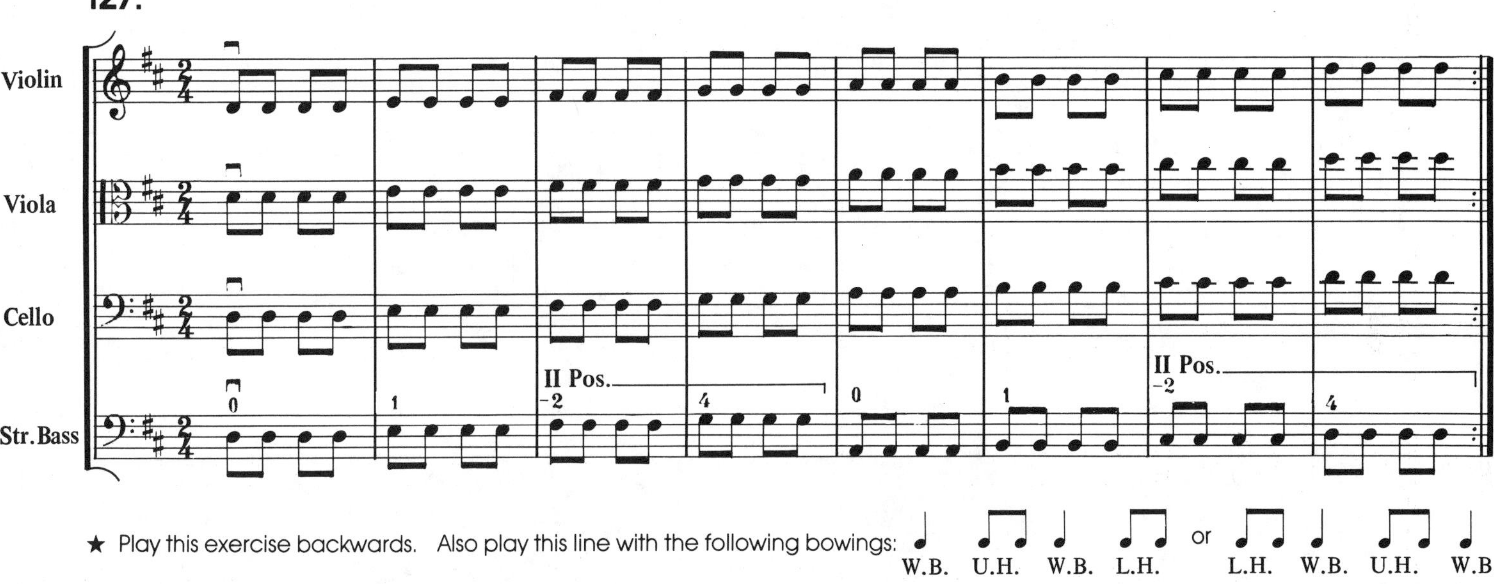

★ Play this exercise backwards. Also play this line with the following bowings: W.B. U.H. W.B. L.H. or L.H. W.B. U.H. W.B.

TEACHER: After everyone has written in the counting, have them clap and count Line 128. Also have them count as they play the same line pizzicato.

THEORY GAME

128. CZECH FOLK SONG

Traditional

Vln. Vla. Cello Str. Bass Pa.

9 10 11 12 13 14 15 16

★ Write in the counting.

TEACHER: It is important to reinforce the system of counting rhythms throughout ALL FOR STRINGS. Refer to score page 25 for COUNTING SYSTEMS FOR RHYTHMS.

129. SHE'LL BE COMIN' 'ROUND THE MOUNTAIN

American Folk Song

Violin Viola Cello Str. Bass Piano

1 2 3 4 5 6 7 8

★ Check your left hand position.

130. LITTLE ANNIE

Czech Folk Song

Violin — L.H. W.B.

Viola — L.H. W.B.

Cello — L.H. W.B.

Str. Bass — L.H. W.B.

Piano

Fine

★ Check the placement of your bow.

THEORY GAME

131. RHYTHM TEASER

1. Write in the counting. 2. Clap and count. 3. Play arco or pizzicato.

TEACHER: Check the playing positions of your string players often. Have the students check each other to make them aware of the important points of holding the bow, holding the instrument, posture and bowing. Refer to student book pages 4-5, score pages 14-21.

TEACHER: Assign for home practice the Bow Grip Exercises found on student book page 4, score pages 22-23. Students will build the strength and flexibility that is needed for a good bow grip through constant repetition of these exercises.

STUDENT BOOK—Page 37

TEACHER: Pick a scale and a bowing and have students play this in various tempos. Refer to student book page 48, score pages 172-174. The playing of fast note values in a fast tempo and slow note values in a slow tempo can be used to build the concepts of proper bow division and bow control.

NEW IDEA

TEMPOS	Andante = moderately slow Moderato = moderate speed Allegro = quick and lively

TEACHER: This is an excellent song to memorize for the development of good bow division and excellent tone production.

132. LONG, LONG AGO

* Memorize

Bayley

★ Also play this song with the following bowing:

TEACHER: The students should work towards the tip in measures 1 and 7 and towards the frog in measures 3 and 5. This will put the bow in the right position to use whole bows on the half notes and final whole note. Strive for a smooth singing style. You may want to play a recording of this concerto for your class.

133. THEME—BEETHOVEN VIOLIN CONCERTO

Beethoven

134. CAN-CAN

Offenbach

★ Check your bow grip often.

135.

★ Draw in the bar lines for each section. Be sure to notice the time signature.

FERMATA (sometimes called a "hold")	𝄐	Play the note until your teacher or director signals you to stop. Play the note longer than written.

136. N. PAGANINI

Paganini

Vln.

Vla.

Cello

Str. Bass

Pa.

6 7 8 9 10

Vln.

Vla.

Cello

Str. Bass

Pa.

11 12 13 14 15 16

THEORY GAME

137. KOOKABURRA

Australian Round

★ This round is written in the following key: ______________________.

138. JOLLY OLD ST. NICK

Traditional

★ This line is written in the following key: ______________.

★ Also play this line pizzicato.

RITARD	*ritard.* or *rit.*	Gradually slow the tempo.

139. THE OLD WOMAN AND THE PEDDLER

English Folk Song-Ensemble

Melody

Violin

Viola

Cello

Str. Bass

Ensemble

Violin

Viola

Cello

Str. Bass

Piano

7 8 ⑨ 10 11 12

Vln.

Vla.

Cello

Str. Bass

rit.

7 8 ⑨ 10 11 12

Vln.

Vla.

Cello

Str. Bass

rit.

7 8 ⑨ 10 11 12

Pa.

rit.

140. RHYTHM TEASER

1. Write in the counting. 2. Clap and count. 3. Play arco or pizzicato.

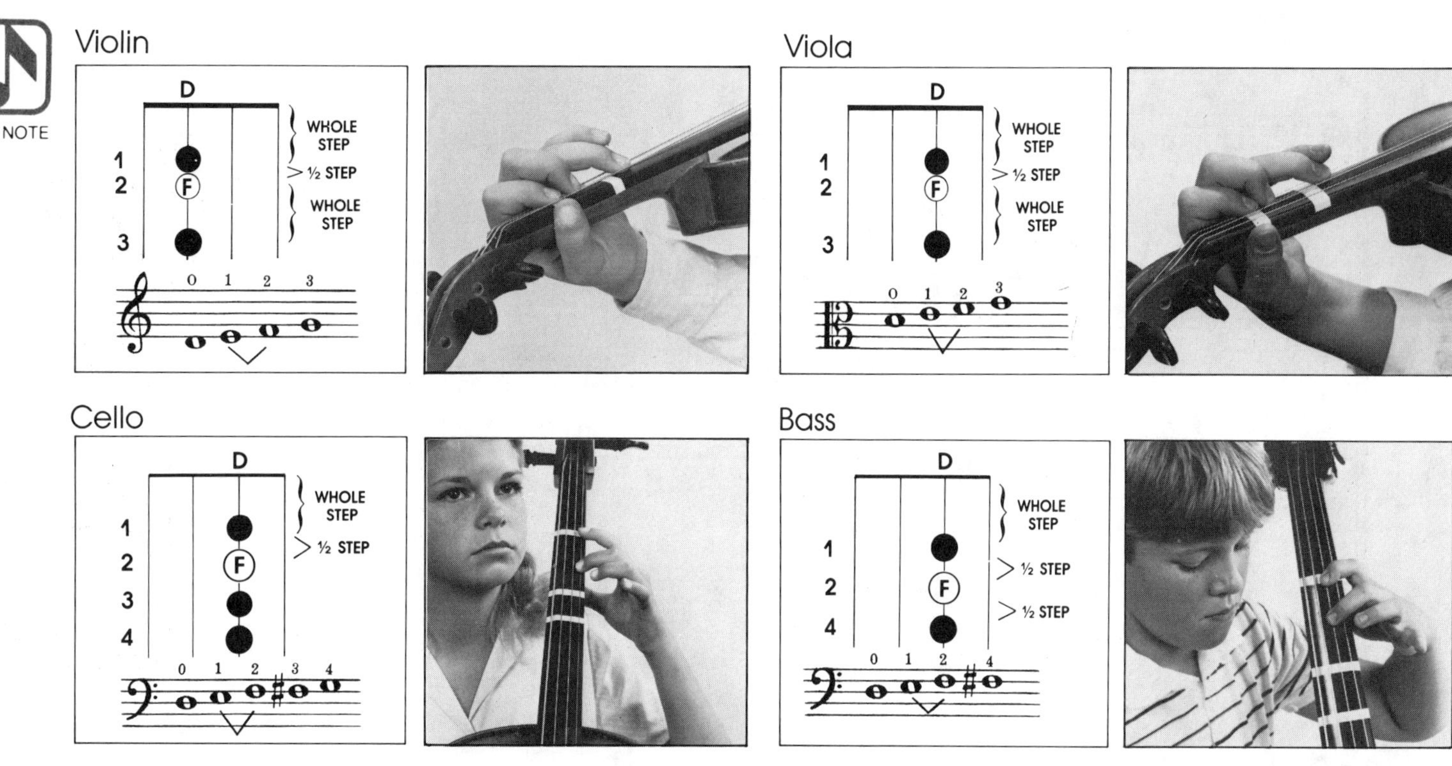

TEACHER: When violin and viola students play F♮ the tendency is to also lower the 1st and 3rd fingers. Stress keeping the 1st and 2nd fingers close and to reach with the 3rd finger.

141. NEW NOTE F♮

Ⓐ

Violin
Viola
Cello
Str. Bass

Ⓑ

Violin
Viola
Cello
Str. Bass

142.

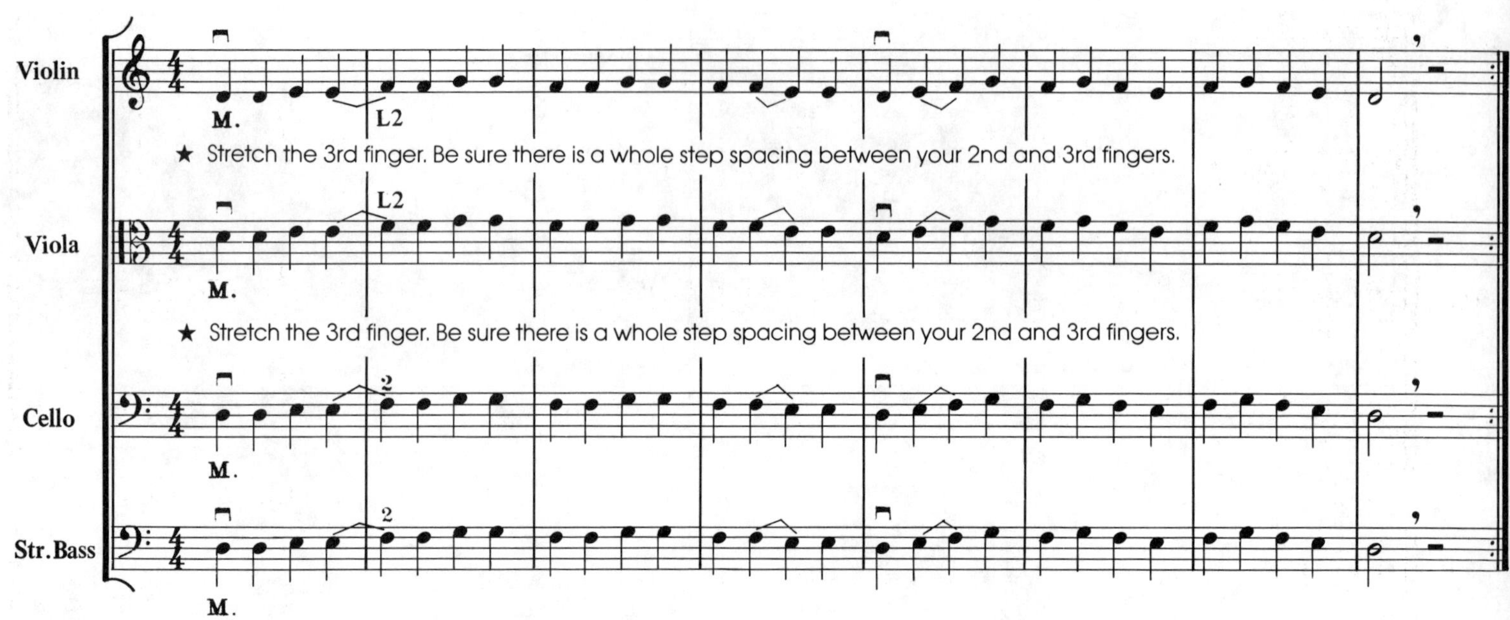
Violin
M.
L2
★ Stretch the 3rd finger. Be sure there is a whole step spacing between your 2nd and 3rd fingers.
Viola
L2
M.
★ Stretch the 3rd finger. Be sure there is a whole step spacing between your 2nd and 3rd fingers.
Cello
2
M.
Str. Bass
2
M.

143.

Violin
Viola
Cello
Str. Bass

★ Also play this line with the following bowing:

TEACHER: You may wish to have students circle all the F♮'s in this line to reinforce this new note.

THEORY GAME

144.

Violin
Viola
Cello
Str. Bass

★ Circle all the F♮'s in this line.

KEY SIGNATURE
When you see this key signature, play all the notes as naturals. This is the key signature for C Major.

145. FOLK SONG

TEACHER: This is an excellent exercise for violin and viola students to master the movement from F♮ to F♯. Sliding this finger back and forth will strengthen this finger. Have students practice each section many times for complete mastery.

146. FINGER TWISTERS

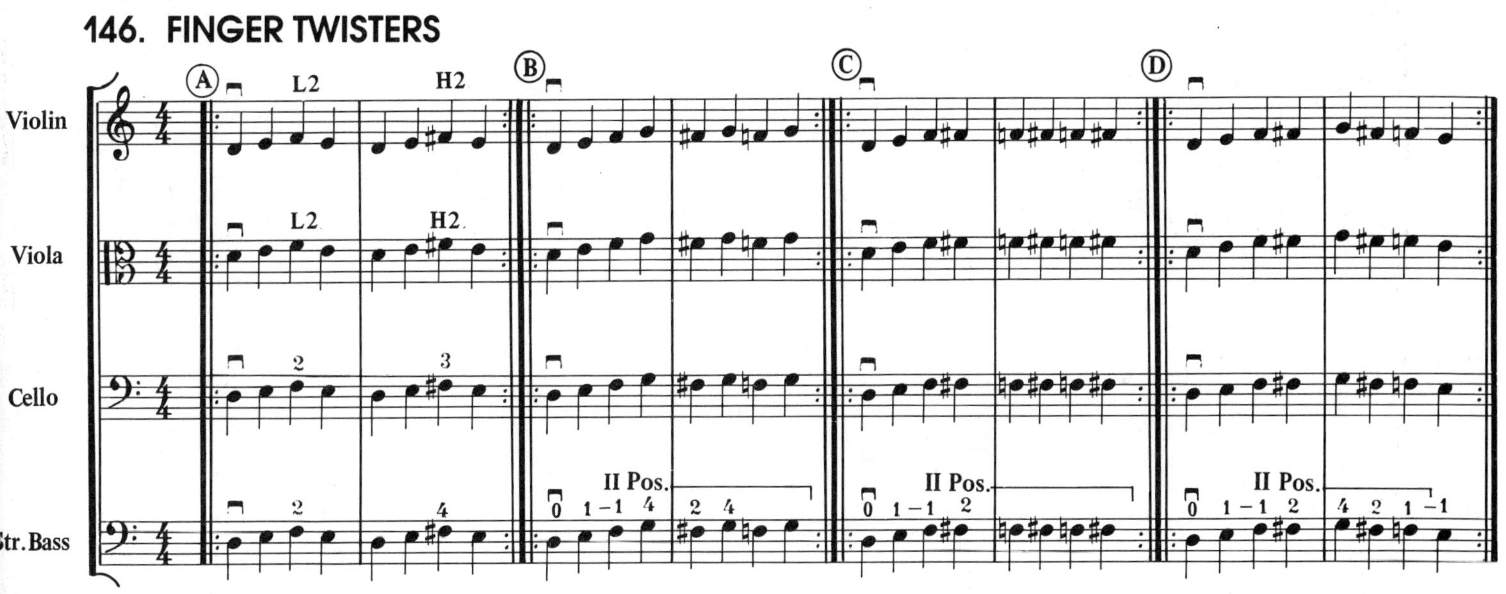

★ Play each section 4 times.

TEACHER: This round is in the key of d minor. Play this round once with F♯'s and again with F♮'s to show the difference between a major key and a minor key.

147. KEEP THE MUSIC RINGING

Hungarian Round

Violin I. L2 II. III.

Viola I. L2 II. III.

Cello I. 2 II. III.

Str. Bass I. 2 II. III.

Piano 1 2 3 4 5 6 7 8

TEACHER: Place the bow at the middle and use the lower half of the bow for the first note.

148. A TISKET A TASKET

Traditional

TEACHER: Have violin and viola students write H or L under the 2nd finger notes to identify the proper placement. Cello and bass students should write the correct finger number of all B's and F's.

149. HI-LO NO. 1

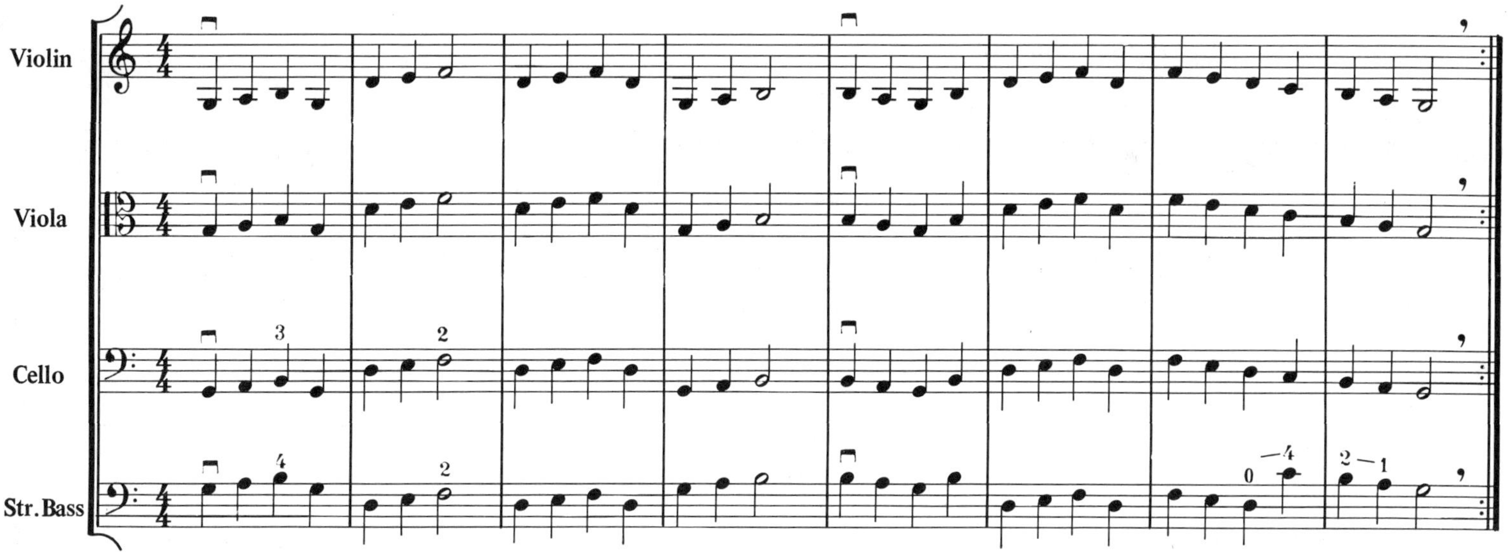

★ Pay special attention to the placement of your 2nd finger in lines 149 and 150.

150. HI-LO NO. 2

★ Also play this line with the following bowing:

THEORY GAME

151. MUSICAL ROAD SIGNS

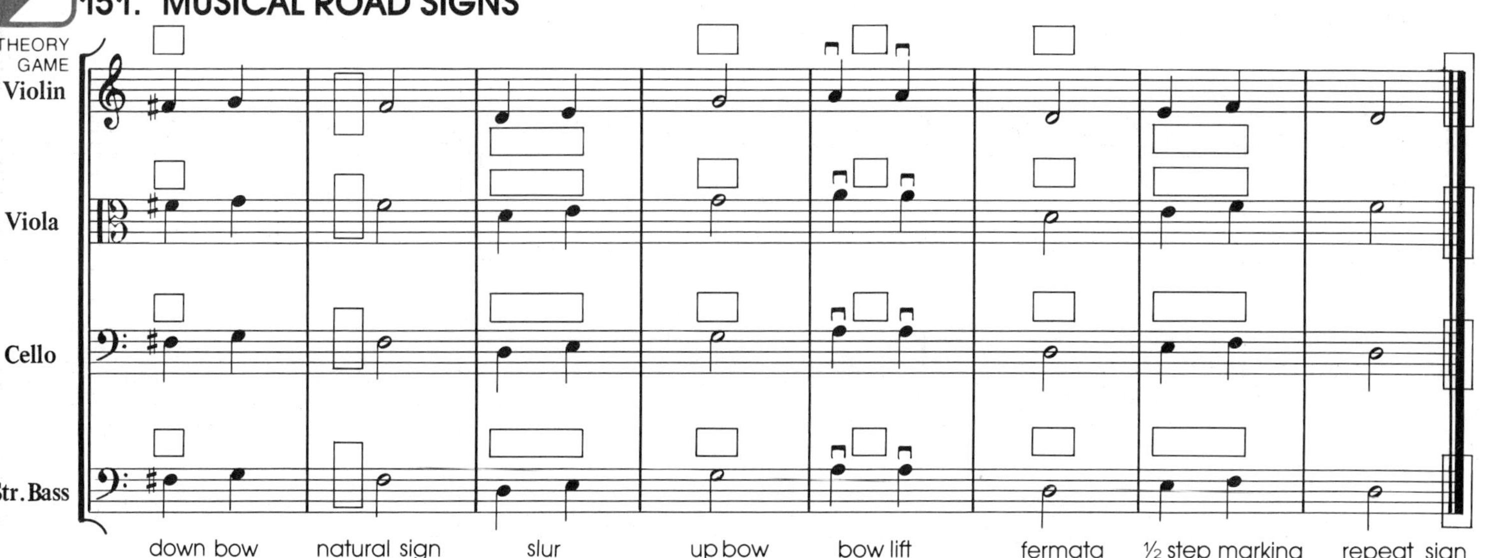

★ Write in the correct musical marking in the box provided.

TEACHER: The basses can play the lower notes by learning C♮ which is introduced on the next page or play the upper notes by shifting.

152. MEXICAN CLAPPING SONG—OH WHERE HAS MY LITTLE DOG GONE

Folk Songs

Vln.
Vla.
Cello
Str. Bass
1.
2.
Vln.
Vla.
Cello
Str. Bass
1.
2.
Pa.
1.
2.

153. SNAKE CHARMER

154. POSITION CHECK

TEACHER: Refer to the POSITION CHECK on score page 93 for the check list of proper instrument and hand positions. It is important to use the check list often so that incorrect positions don't become habits.

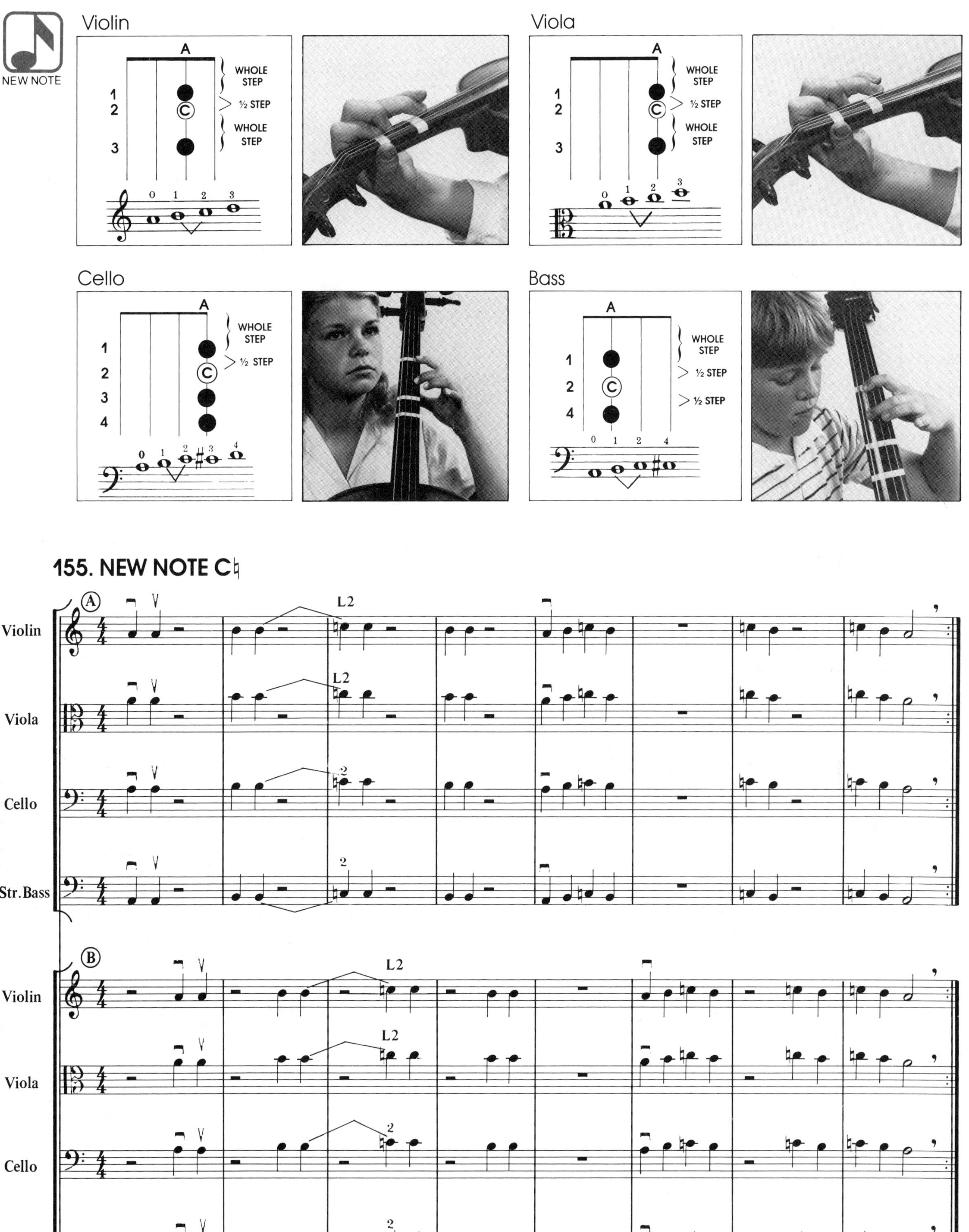
NEW NOTE
Violin
A
WHOLE STEP
½ STEP
WHOLE STEP
1
2
3
Viola
A
WHOLE STEP
½ STEP
WHOLE STEP
Cello
A
WHOLE STEP
½ STEP
1
2
3
4
Bass
A
WHOLE STEP
½ STEP
½ STEP
1
2
4
155. NEW NOTE C♮
Violin
Viola
Cello
Str. Bass
L2

156.

TEACHER: Remind the students to use a very slow bow for the whole notes. Practice this line with the written rhythm on open strings so the students can concentrate on their bowing.

157. SOME FOLKS DO

Foster

Violin
L2

Viola
L2

Cello
2

Str.Bass
4 1

Piano

158.

Violin
L2

Viola
L2 L2

Cello
2 2

Str.Bass
2 2

159. BOW TWISTER

TEACHER: Remind the students to lift appropriate fingers from one string and place them across on the next string and back again. Do not let them flatten fingers to play the note across the string. Practicing this technique faithfully will develop finger strength and independence. Be sure students leave fingers down where indicated.

160. TECHNIC TRAINER

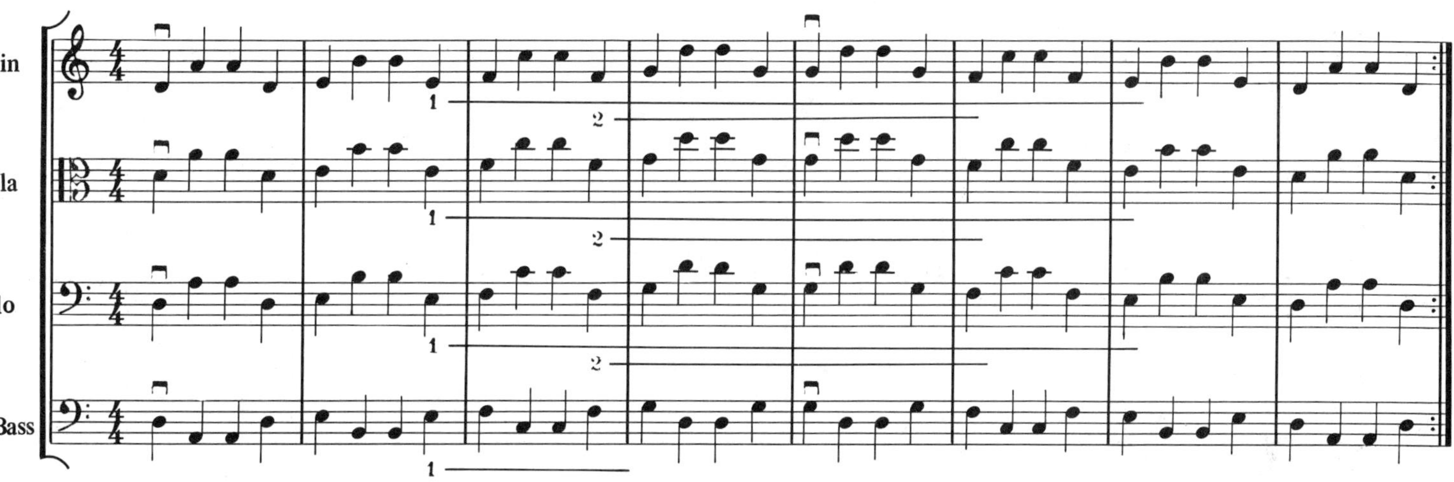

TEACHER: This is an excellent exercise for violin and viola players to master the movement from C♮ to C♯. Sliding this finger back and forth will strengthen this finger. Have students practice each section many times for complete mastery.

161. FINGER TWISTER

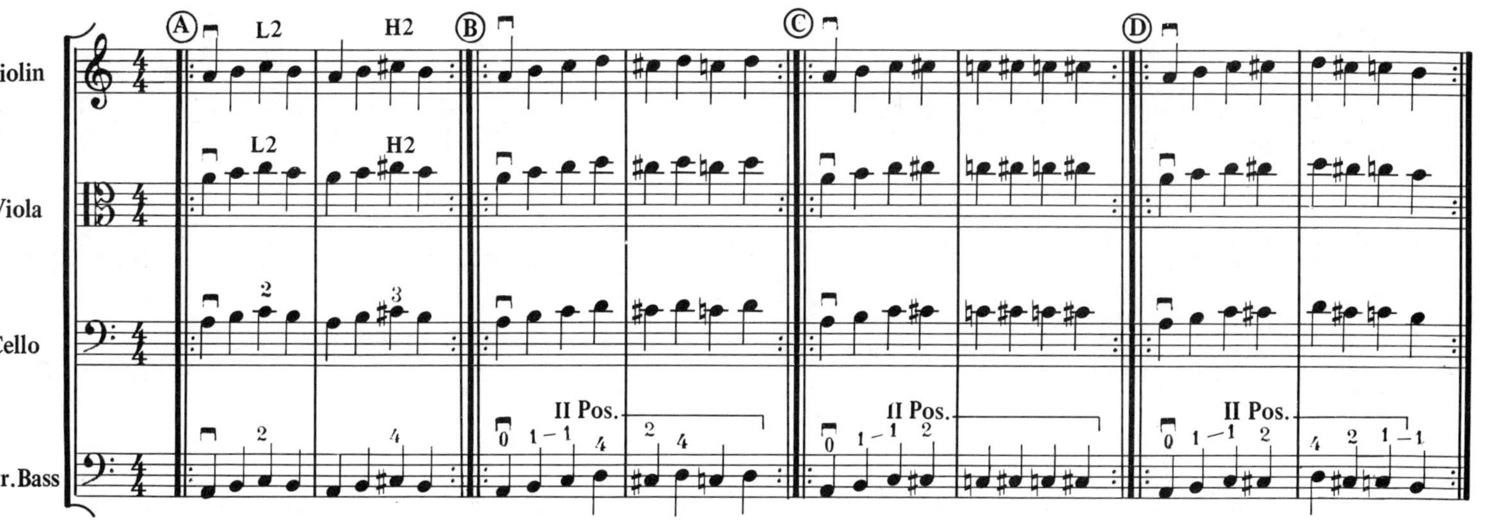

★ Play each section 4 times.

DYNAMICS			
	f	= *forte*	= Loud
	mf	= *mezzo forte*	= Medium loud
	p	= *piano*	= Soft

TEACHER: Dynamics are important for expression in music. Dynamics are produced with the following techniques:

	forte	*piano*
Bow Speed	fast	slow
Bow Placement	close to bridge	close to fingerboard
Bow Weight	much arm weight	less arm weight
Bow Hair	more hair against string	less hair against string

162. CANON

Tallis

Violin
Viola
Cello
Str. Bass
Piano

I. II. III. IV. *mf*

163. FRENCH FOLK SONG

* Memorize

Violin
Viola
Cello
II Pos.
Str. Bass
Piano

f

1 2 3 4 ⑤ 6

★ Be sure to use good bow division.

Vln.
Vla.
Cello
Str.Bass
Pa.
p
mf
f

TEACHER: Periodically check the fine tuners to make sure that they are not digging into the tops of the instruments. Loosen the adjusting screw and bring the string up to pitch using the peg. This process will allow enough turns in the adjusting screw to handle many more tunings.

TEACHER: Class warm-ups can be used effectively to reinforce many of the concepts previously taught. Consider follow-up work on slurs, bow division, tempo changes and dynamics. Although scales serve as excellent material for this purpose, consider playing familiar songs or melodies with a new string technique.

164. BRIDGE AT AVIGNON

French Folk Song

TEACHER: Time must be permitted for instrument care. Devote a small block of time to a good cleaning session. A good cleaner polish and several pieces of cloth can be used to polish the instruments. Old English Scratch Cover can be used to cover some of the nicks and scrapes in old instruments. Mid-year is a good time to recommend that students launder their cleaning cloth to remove rosin.

TEACHER: One value of shifting is to extend the playing range on the instrument. Another value is in keeping a fingering passage on one string making it easier without the string crossing. Such is the case for the string bass in the first eight measures of the harmony part.

165. THERE'S MUSIC IN THE AIR

Root-Ensemble

9
10
11
12
13
14
15
16
Vln.
Vla.
Cello
Str. Bass
Pa.
mf
f

TEACHER: The FINGERING REVIEW provides an opportunity to remind students about use of accidentals and how the bar lines and double bars lines will affect them.

THEORY GAME

166. FINGERING REVIEW

① Write in the fingering, either H2 or L2, under each note.
② In the fingering chart above, write the name of the note that is played at the place of each circle.

① Write in the fingering, either H2 or L2, under each note.
② In the fingering chart above, write the name of the note that is played at the place of each circle.

① Write in the fingering, either 2 or 3, under each note.
② In the fingering chart above, write the name of the note that is played at the place of each circle.

① Write in the fingering, either 2 or 4, under each note.
② In the fingering chart above, write the name of the note that is played at the place of each circle.

Violin

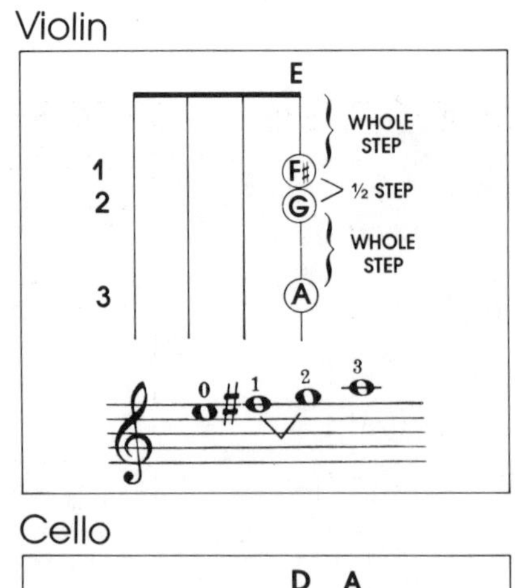

Viola

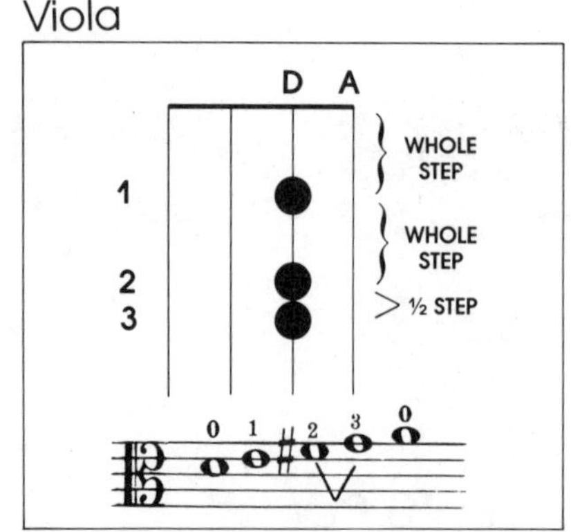

Cello

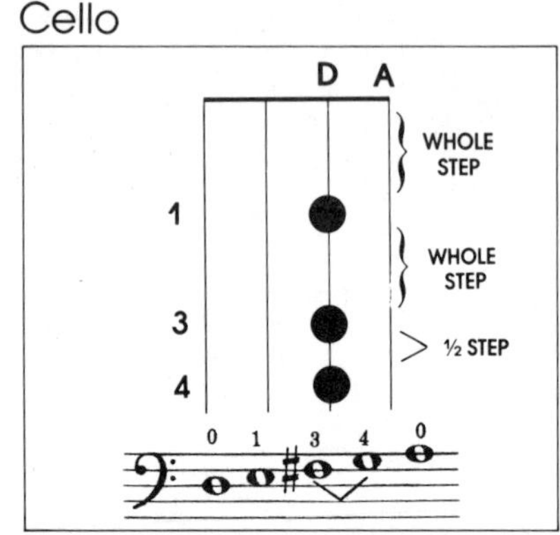

Bass

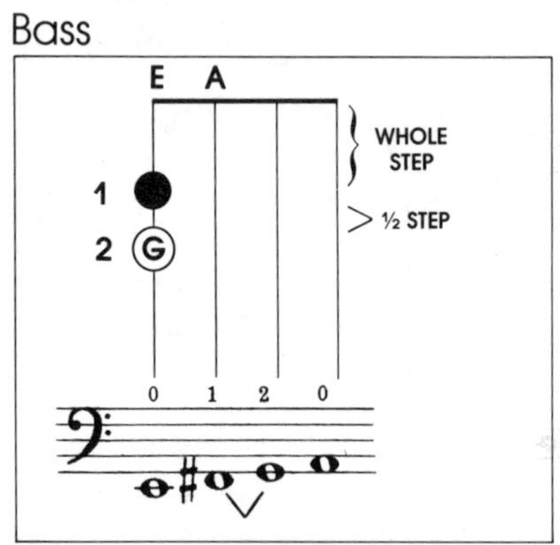

TEACHER: Check the hand positions of all violin students. Be sure the fingers come straight down on the string with the elbow under the violin. The bass students will need a well rosined bow to play on the E string. Have them use more arm weight and pull a slower bow for this thick string. They may also need to turn the bass to the left to make it more comfortable to bow without hitting their leg. The viola and cellos review their notes on the D string.

167. NEW NOTES F♯ AND G

Ⓐ

Violin

Viola

Cello

Str. Bass

L2

2

Ⓑ

Violin

Viola

Cello

Str. Bass

L2

2

TEACHER: NEW NOTE A is specially written for the violins learning this new note on their E string. Everyone can enjoy this exercise with this new bowing: etc.

168. NEW NOTE A

169. TECHNIC TRAINER

TEACHER: Violin and viola players should analyze the finger spacing from one note to the next throughout the broken thirds section of Line 170. If they understand the finger spacing they will play with better intonation.

170. G MAJOR SCALE WITH BROKEN THIRDS

Also play this exercise substituting the correct number of eighth notes for each written note:

★ Refer to page 48 for other bowing and scale possibilities.

TEACHER: Ask all students to find the tonic and dominant arpeggios in this selection.

171. ARPEGGIO FUN

★ Also play this song slurring three quarter notes as follows:

TEACHER: All selections on student page 44 make excellent solo material. Encourage everyone to work on all of the techniques that go into a polished performance.

Tone	Tempo
Intonation	Dynamics
Bow Division	Phrasing

THEORY GAME

172. WHEN LOVE IS KIND

Irish Folk Song

★ This line is written in the following key:____________.

TEACHER: Have the students work towards the frog before the tied note in measures 1, 3, 7 and 15. Then the bow will be in position to use a whole bow for each long note.

173. SAINTS

Traditional

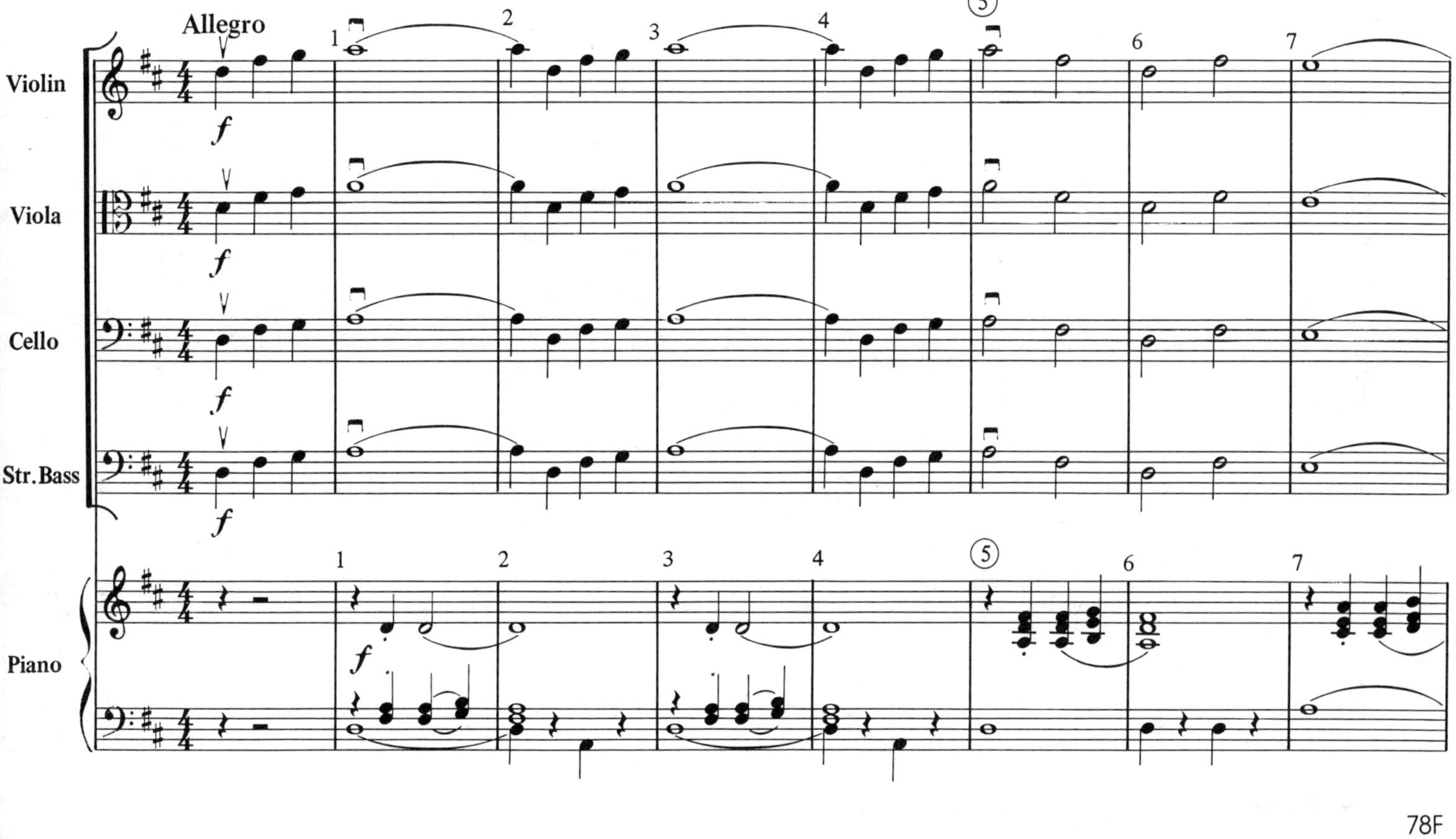

Allegro

Violin

Viola

Cello

Str.Bass

Piano

f

1 2 3 4 5 6 7

Vln.
Vla.
Cello
Str. Bass
Pa.

TEACHER: Measures 1-8 are in unison. Measures 9-16 are written as a duet. Violins and violas have the melody and the cellos and basses have the harmony.

THEORY GAME

174. SKIP TO MY LOU

American Folk Song

Moderato

Violin
Viola
Cello
Str. Bass
Piano

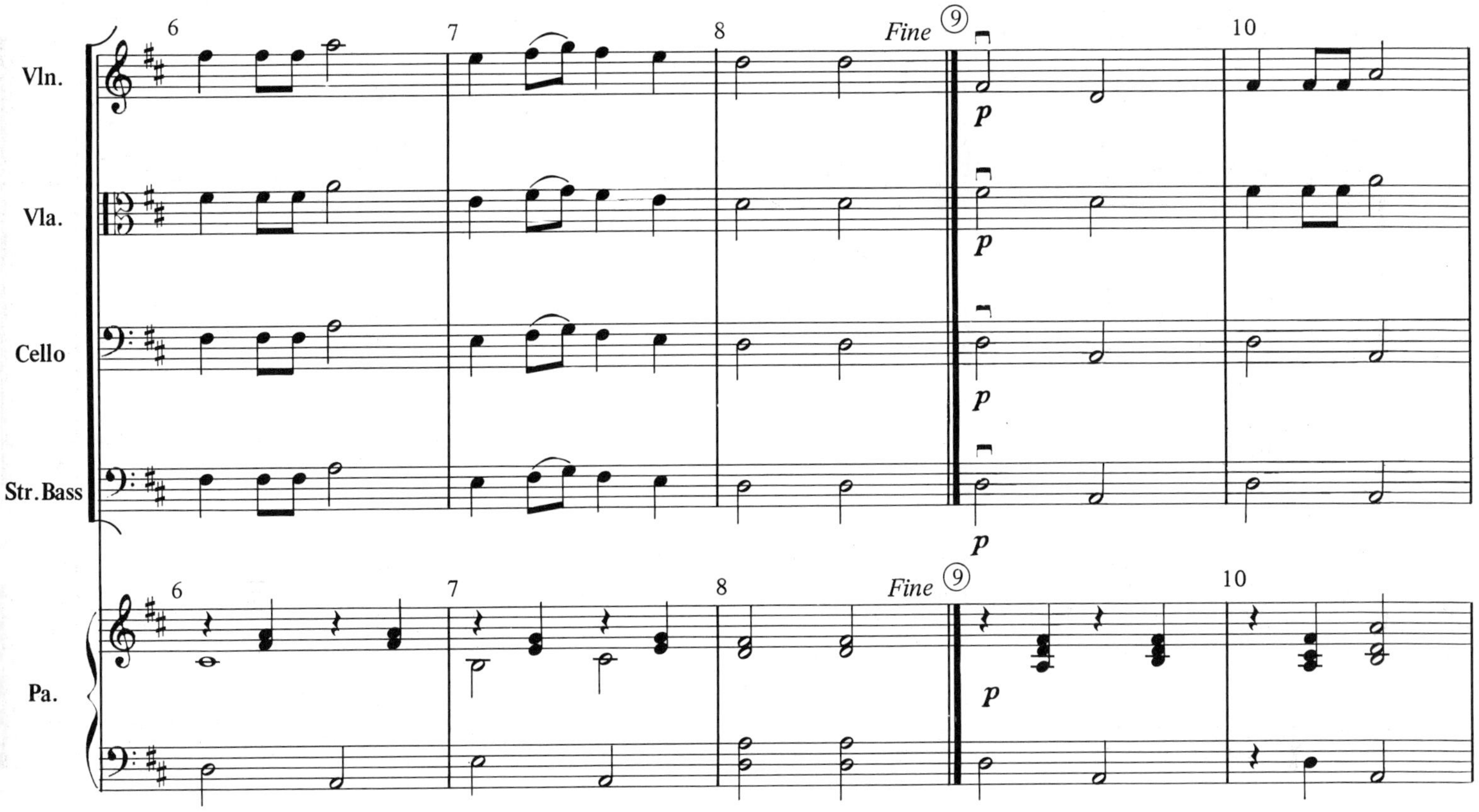

6 7 8 *Fine* 9 10

Vln.

p

Vla.

p

Cello

p

Str. Bass

p

6 7 8 *Fine* 9 10

Pa.

p

★ This line is written in the following key:_______________.

175. SHEPHERD'S HEY

English Folk Song

Moderato

Violin *mf* *Fine*

Viola *mf*

Cello *mf*

Str. Bass *mf*

Piano *mf* *Fine*

Violin

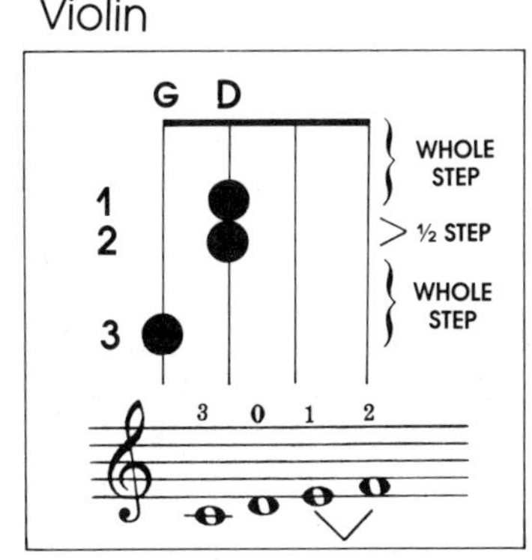

Viola

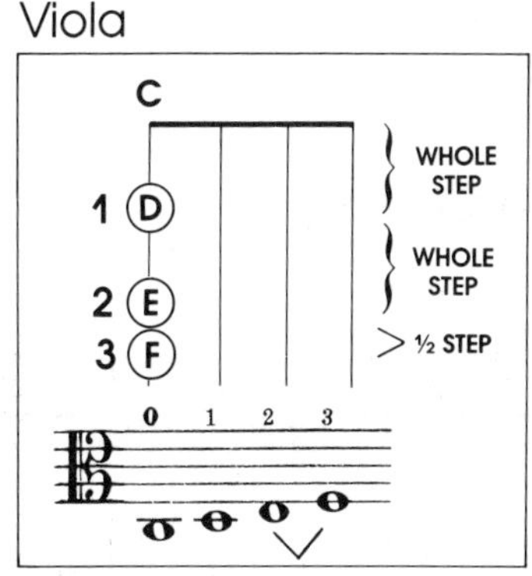

Cello

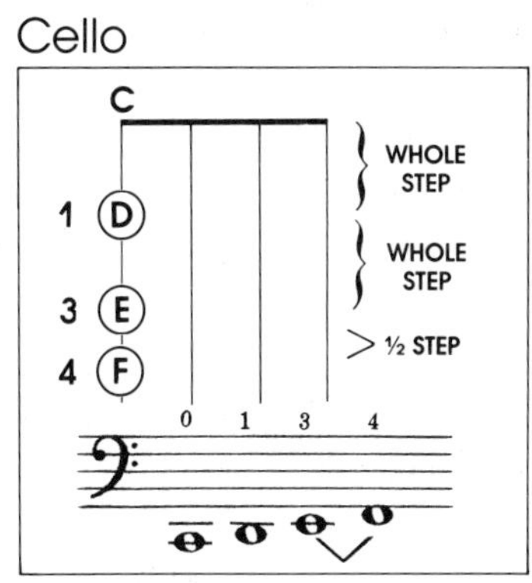

Bass

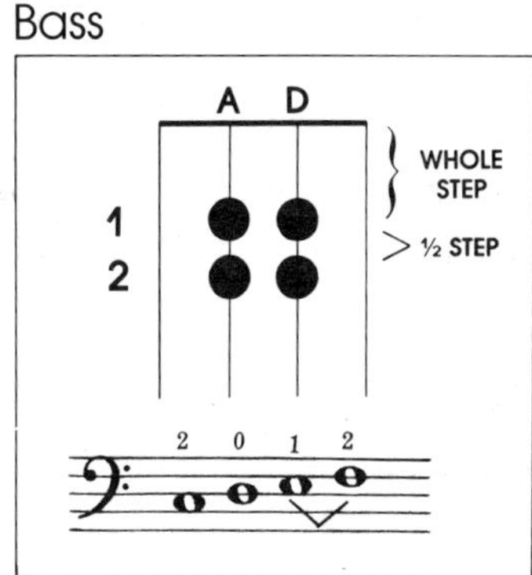

TEACHER: Remind the viola and cello players that playing on the C string (the thickest string) requires a slower bow stroke with more arm weight for the bow. The violin and string bass players have review notes.

176. NEW NOTES C, D AND E (violas and cellos play on their C string)

(A)

Violin

Viola

Cello

Str. Bass

(B)

Violin

Viola

Cello

Str. Bass

TEACHER: Only viola and cello players have new note F to learn.

177. NEW NOTE F

★ Also play this line with the following bowing: 

TEACHER: The concept of putting down all fingers involving a skip and the concept of leaving all fingers down need frequent repetition and reminders. Use these principles often to improve intonation.

178.

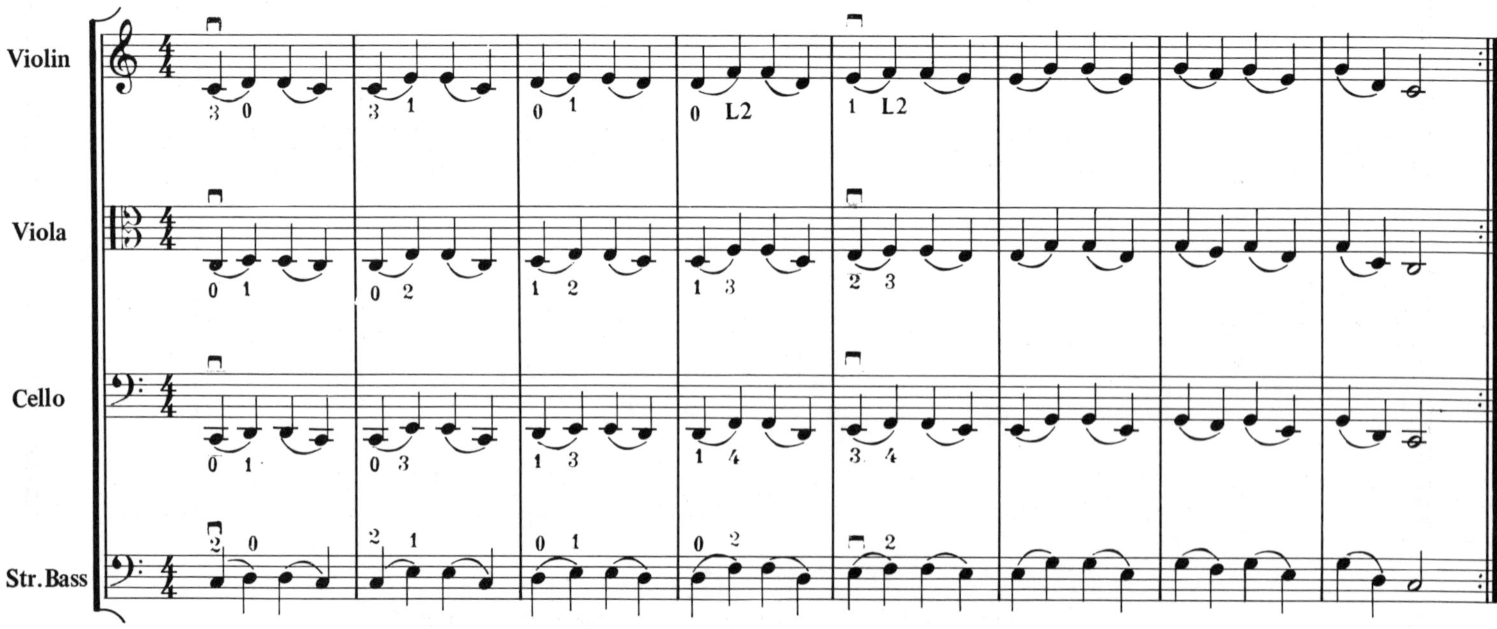

★ Also play this line with separate bows.

TEACHER: Violin and bass students may need to prepare the first note of this exercise for good intonation.

179. C MAJOR SCALE WITH BROKEN THIRDS

★ Also play this exercise with the following bowings: a. b. c.

★ Refer to page 48 for other bowing and scale possibilities.

180. ARPEGGIO FUN

Vln.

Vla.

Cello

Str. Bass

Pa.

★ Also play this line slurring the three quarter notes: 

TEACHER: Explain to the students that this duet is written in two keys which is a technique that many modern composers use. This selection will have quite a different and interesting sound.

181. DUET IN TWO KEYS

Frost-Duet

1. The A part is written in the following key:___________.

2. The B part is written in the following key:___________.

THEME AND VARIATIONS	A simple tune followed by the same tune with changes.

TEACHER: Many additional bowing variations are possible with this THEME AND VARIATIONS. See student page 48, score page 174 for suggestions. Variation 2 may also be played pizzicato. Viola and cello players could also transpose their lines either up or down an octave for additional practice.

182. THEME AND VARIATIONS

Anderson

Theme

Violin
Viola
Cello
Str. Bass
Piano

mf

Fine

Variation 1

Vln.
Vla.
Cello
Str. Bass
Pa.

f

Variation 2

Vln. *p*
Vla. *p*
Cello *p*
Str. Bass *p*
Pa. *p*

Variation 3

D.C. AL CODA	*D. C.* (Da Capo) = to the beginning *al Coda* = to Coda *Coda* = ending	When you see the *D. C. al Coda* go back to the beginning. When you come to the ⊕ (Coda sign) skip to the Coda.

TEACHER: Explain the meaning of divisi. Note that the student book violin parts are written on a single staff. Divide as necessary to achieve good balance. This is an excellent program selection.

183. HAPPY BLUES

Frost

Allegro moderato

Violins 1, 2 · Viola (div.) · Cello (pizz.) · Str. Bass (pizz.) · Piano

Vlns. 1, 2 · Vla. · Cello · Str. Bass · Piano

to Coda
11
12
13
14
15
Vlns.
1
2
Vla.
Cello
Str. Bass
p
p
p
p
p
to Coda
Pa.
p
16
17
18
19
20

Vlns. 1 2
Vla.
Cello
Str. Bass
Pa.

21 22 23 24 25

mf

Vlns. 1 2
Vla.
Cello
Str. Bass
Pa.

26 27 28 29 30

31
32
33
34
35
Vlns.
1
2
Vla.
Cello
Str. Bass
Pa.
36
D.C. al Fine
Coda
37
38
39
40
pizz.
2
3
4

TEACHER: JAZZ FEATURE is written so that any string section or any individual can be featured in a solo. Line A is the solo line. Each instrument has a different solo line which is constructed of basically two different rhythms and only one solo line A should be used at a time. Line B consists of blues chords written divisi for three parts and should be used as accompaniment for the solo line. A mixed instrument class could use the large notes for a satisfying distribution of parts. All three parts of each chord are cued so that complete harmonies are possible with a limited instrumentation. Use your imagination! Many possibilities exist with this feature.

184. JAZZ FEATURE

Anderson

Rhythm patterns for the B part:

★ Play pizzicato.

1. 2. 3. 4.

7
8
9
10
11
12
Vln.
Vla.
Cello
Str. Bass
7
8
9
10
11
12
Vln.
Vla.
Cello
Str. Bass

TECHNIC DEVELOPMENT

TEACHER: The following pages may be used shortly after the notes of each scale are introduced. The bowings at the bottom of page 48 in the student books are numbered so that reference and assignments can be easily made, i.e. play the D Major scale with bowing 7.

Be sure the students play the various bowings and rhythms with good bow division.

Alternate notes are provided for the broken third studies. Use the pitch that best fits your needs.

Several lines of the string bass book go into 3rd position which is not covered in Book 1. However, with a few minutes of special instruction, most bass students should be able to play the scales and broken thirds that go into 3rd position.

1. D MAJOR SCALE

2. D MAJOR BROKEN THIRDS

3. G MAJOR SCALE

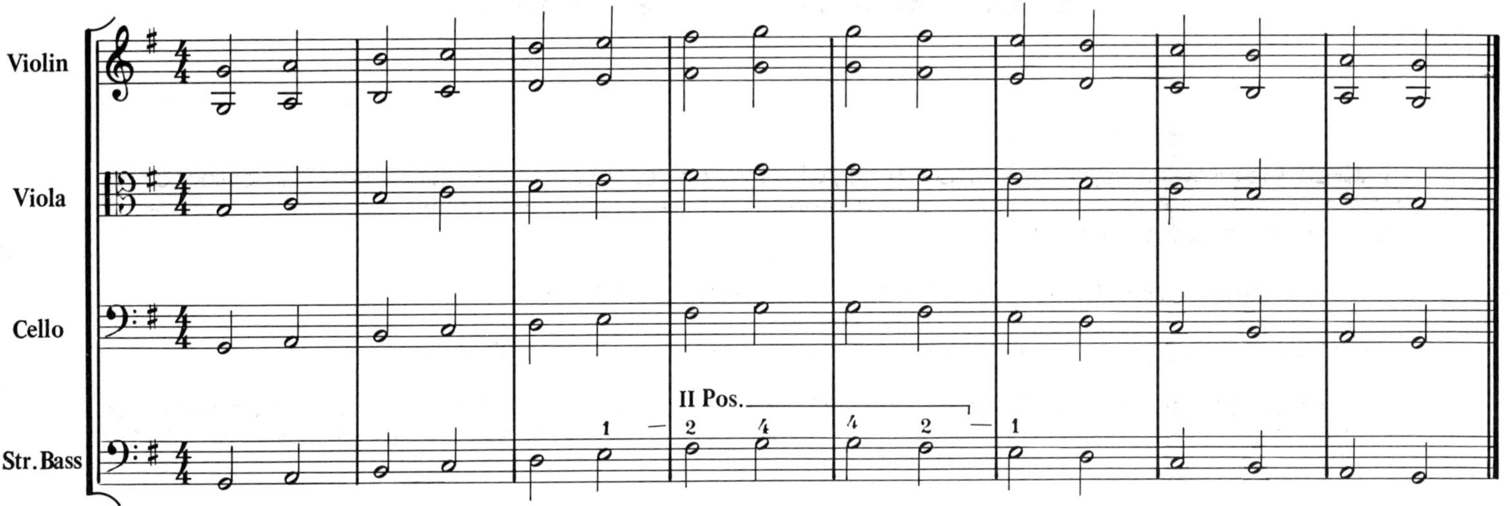

4. G MAJOR BROKEN THIRDS

5. C MAJOR SCALE

6. C MAJOR BROKEN THIRDS

Play the scales and broken thirds with the rhythms and bowings listed below. Be sure to play these rhythms and bowings with good bow division.

Bow Divisions:

Whole Bow = W. B. Upper Half = U. H. Lower Half = L. H. Middle = M.

$\frac{4}{4}$

1.
2.
3.
4.
5.
6.
7.
8. Slur 4 notes

$\frac{2}{4}$

9.
10.
11.
12.
13.
14.
15.
16. Slur 2 notes

$\frac{3}{4}$

17.
18.
19.
20.
21.
22.
23.
24. Slur 3 notes

GLOSSARY

BASICS

STAFF		five lines and four spaces on which music is written
TREBLE CLEF		used for violin (high range)
SHARP	♯	raises a note ½ step
NATURAL	♮	cancels a sharp
KEY SIGNATURES		sharps at the beginning of a piece that change certain notes throughout the piece
PICK-UP NOTES		note(s) that come before the first full measure of a piece
REPEAT SIGN		play the previous section of music again
FIRST AND SECOND ENDINGS	1. 2.	play the first ending the first time. Then repeat the same music, skip the first ending, and play the second ending.
TIE		a curved line that connects two notes of the **same** pitch. Hold the note for the combined value of the two notes.
FERMATA ("HOLD")	𝄐	play the note longer than written. Play the note until your teacher or director signals you to stop.
RITARD	*rit. or ritard*	gradually slow the tempo
DA CAPO AL FINE	*D.C. al Fine*	go back to the beginning and stop when you come to the Fine
DA CAPO AL CODA	*D.C. al Coda*	go back to the beginning. When you come to Coda sign 𝄌, skip to the coda.
DAL SEGNO AL FINE	*D.S. al Fine*	go back to the 𝄋 sign and stop when you come to Fine
SOLO	solo	only one person plays
ENSEMBLE		a group usually playing different parts
DIVISI	div.	part of the section plays the top note; part plays the bottom note

BOWINGS

ARCO	*arco*	play with the bow
PIZZICATO	*pizz.*	pluck the string
DOWN BOW	⊓	move the bow toward the tip
UP BOW	V	move the bow toward the frog
BOW LIFT	,	lift the bow and return it to the lower half or frog of the bow
SLUR		play 2 or more different notes with one bow. The sound should be smooth and continuous.
WHOLE BOW	W.B.	play with a full bow
LOWER HALF	L.H.	play in the lower half of the bow
UPPER HALF	U.H.	play in the upper half of the bow
MIDDLE OF BOW	M.	play in the middle of the bow
SLURRED STACCATO		a series of **separated** notes played while the bow moves in one direction
LOURÉ		a series of **connected** notes distinctly pulsed while the bow moves in one direction

DYNAMIC AND TEMPO MARKINGS

FORTE	***f***	full volume	**ANDANTE**	**Andante**	moderately slow
MEZZO FORTE	***mf***	medium full volume	**MODERATO**	**Moderato**	moderate speed
PIANO	***p***	soft volume	**ALLEGRO**	**Allegro**	quick and lively

GLOSSARY

BASICS

STAFF		five lines and four spaces on which music is written
ALTO CLEF		used for viola
SHARP	♯	raises a note ½ step
NATURAL	♮	cancels a sharp
KEY SIGNATURES		sharps at the beginning of a piece that change certain notes throughout the piece
PICK-UP NOTES		note(s) that come before the first full measure of a piece
REPEAT SIGN		play the previous section of music again
FIRST AND SECOND ENDINGS	1. 2.	play the first ending the first time. Then repeat the same music, skip the first ending, and play the second ending.
TIE		a curved line that connects two notes of the **same** pitch. Hold the note for the combined value of the two notes.
FERMATA ("HOLD")	𝄐	play the note longer than written. Play the note until your teacher or director signals you to stop.
RITARD	*rit. or ritard*	gradually slow the tempo
DA CAPO AL FINE	*D.C. al Fine*	go back to the beginning and stop when you come to the Fine
DA CAPO AL CODA	*D.C. al Coda*	go back to the beginning. When you come to Coda sign 𝄌, skip to the coda.
DAL SEGNO AL FINE	*D.S. al Fine*	go back to the 𝄋 sign and stop when you come to Fine
SOLO	solo	only one person plays
ENSEMBLE		a group usually playing different parts
DIVISI	div.	part of the section plays the top note; part plays the bottom note

BOWINGS

ARCO	*arco*	play with the bow
PIZZICATO	*pizz.*	pluck the string
DOWN BOW	⊓	move the bow toward the tip
UP BOW	V	move the bow toward the frog
BOW LIFT	,	lift the bow and return it to the lower half or frog of the bow
SLUR		play 2 or more different notes with one bow. The sound should be smooth and continuous.
WHOLE BOW	W.B.	play with a full bow
LOWER HALF	L.H.	play in the lower half of the bow
UPPER HALF	U.H.	play in the upper half of the bow
MIDDLE OF BOW	M.	play in the middle of the bow
SLURRED STACCATO		a series of **separated** notes played while the bow moves in one direction
LOURÉ		a series of **connected** notes distinctly pulsed while the bow moves in one direction

DYNAMIC AND TEMPO MARKINGS

FORTE	*f*	full volume	ANDANTE	Andante	moderately slow
MEZZO FORTE	*mf*	medium full volume	MODERATO	Moderato	moderate speed
PIANO	*p*	soft volume	ALLEGRO	Allegro	quick and lively

Cello

GLOSSARY

BASICS

STAFF		five lines and four spaces on which music is written
BASS CLEF		used for cello
SHARP	♯	raises a note ½ step
NATURAL	♮	cancels a sharp
KEY SIGNATURES		sharps at the beginning of a piece that change certain notes throughout the piece
PICK-UP NOTES		note(s) that come before the first full measure of a piece
REPEAT SIGN		play the previous section of music again
FIRST AND SECOND ENDINGS	1. 2.	play the first ending the first time. Then repeat the same music, skip the first ending, and play the second ending.
TIE		a curved line that connects two notes of the **same** pitch. Hold the note for the combined value of the two notes.
FERMATA ("HOLD")	𝄐	play the note longer than written. Play the note until your teacher or director signals you to stop.
RITARD	*rit. or ritard*	gradually slow the tempo
DA CAPO AL FINE	*D.C. al Fine*	go back to the beginning and stop when you come to the Fine
DA CAPO AL CODA	*D.C. al Coda*	go back to the beginning. When you come to Coda sign 𝄌, skip to the coda.
DAL SEGNO AL FINE	*D.S. al Fine*	go back to the 𝄋 sign and stop when you come to Fine
SOLO	solo	only one person plays
ENSEMBLE		a group usually playing different parts
DIVISI	div.	part of the section plays the top note; part plays the bottom note

BOWINGS

ARCO	*arco*	play with the bow
PIZZICATO	*pizz.*	pluck the string
DOWN BOW	⊓	move the bow toward the tip
UP BOW	V	move the bow toward the frog
BOW LIFT	,	lift the bow and return it to the lower half or frog of the bow
SLUR		play 2 or more different notes with one bow. The sound should be smooth and continuous.
WHOLE BOW	W.B.	play with a full bow
LOWER HALF	L.H.	play in the lower half of the bow
UPPER HALF	U.H.	play in the upper half of the bow
MIDDLE OF BOW	M.	play in the middle of the bow
SLURRED STACCATO		a series of **separated** notes played while the bow moves in one direction
LOURÉ		a series of **connected** notes distinctly pulsed while the bow moves in one direction

DYNAMIC AND TEMPO MARKINGS

FORTE	*f*	full volume	ANDANTE	Andante	moderately slow
MEZZO FORTE	*mf*	medium full volume	MODERATO	Moderato	moderate speed
PIANO	*p*	soft volume	ALLEGRO	Allegro	quick and lively

GLOSSARY

BASICS

STAFF		five lines and four spaces on which music is written
BASS CLEF	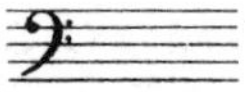	used for string bass
SHARP	♯	raises a note ½ step
NATURAL	♮	cancels a sharp
KEY SIGNATURES		sharps at the beginning of a piece that change certain notes throughout the piece
PICK-UP NOTES		note(s) that come before the first full measure of a piece
REPEAT SIGN	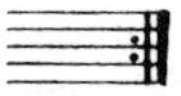	play the previous section of music again
FIRST AND SECOND ENDINGS	 1. 2.	play the first ending the first time. Then repeat the same music, skip the first ending, and play the second ending.
TIE		a curved line that connects two notes of the **same** pitch. Hold the note for the combined value of the two notes.
FERMATA ("HOLD")	𝄐	play the note longer than written. Play the note until your teacher or director signals you to stop.
RITARD	*rit. or ritard*	gradually slow the tempo
DA CAPO AL FINE	*D.C. al Fine*	go back to the beginning and stop when you come to the Fine
DA CAPO AL CODA	*D.C. al Coda*	go back to the beginning. When you come to Coda sign 𝄌, skip to the coda.
DAL SEGNO AL FINE	*D.S. al Fine*	go back to the 𝄋 sign and stop when you come to Fine
SOLO	solo	only one person plays
ENSEMBLE		a group usually playing different parts
DIVISI	div.	part of the section plays the top note; part plays the bottom note

BOWINGS

ARCO	*arco*	play with the bow
PIZZICATO	*pizz.*	pluck the string
DOWN BOW	⊓	move the bow toward the tip
UP BOW	V	move the bow toward the frog
BOW LIFT	❜	lift the bow and return it to the lower half or frog of the bow
SLUR		play 2 or more different notes with one bow. The sound should be smooth and continuous.
WHOLE BOW	W.B.	play with a full bow
LOWER HALF	L.H.	play in the lower half of the bow
UPPER HALF	U.H.	play in the upper half of the bow
MIDDLE OF BOW	M.	play in the middle of the bow
SLURRED STACCATO		a series of **separated** notes played while the bow moves in one direction
LOURÉ		a series of **connected** notes distinctly pulsed while the bow moves in one direction

DYNAMIC AND TEMPO MARKINGS

FORTE	*f*	full volume	ANDANTE	Andante	moderately slow
MEZZO FORTE	*mf*	medium full volume	MODERATO	Moderato	moderate speed
PIANO	*p*	soft volume	ALLEGRO	Allegro	quick and lively

RECRUITING

INSTRUMENT DEMONSTRATION

Instrument demonstrations, which may range from performance/demonstrations for individual classrooms to performance/demonstrations for all-school assemblies, provide an excellent means of interesting students in playing instruments.

Such demonstrations may take various forms. They may be presented by the orchestra from the school, by a small group of students, by private teachers in the area, by a combination of students and teachers, by professional performers, or by your friends or colleagues. These programs provide an opportunity to **show** and **demonstrate** each instrument. The best way of capturing student interest is by playing small excerpts of familiar melodies, popular songs, television theme songs or commercial tunes.

For obvious reasons, the speakers must emphasize the fact that **all** instruments are needed to make an orchestra. Instruments which are the least popular should be given more importance in the demonstration and discussion.

Students should be told how to become a part of the exciting world of instrumental music. If the demonstration is presented with enthusiasm, students in the audience will respond positively and will want to join the orchestra program.

PARENTS' MEETING

A parents' meeting can be a very important part of the recruiting program. Such a meeting is usually held in the evening, with both parents and students invited to participate. At this time, many aspects of the beginning string instrumental music program and the total program may be explained, including the following:

1) The value of the instrumental music program.
2) A description of the beginning instrumental music program.
3) A description of the total instrumental music program.
4) Details about joining the program and the forming of classes.

Recruiting students into the instrumental music program is one of your most important activities. Because the ultimate success of the program is directly related to both the **quality** and the **quantity** of the students recruited, a great deal of thought and planning must go into the recruiting activities.

There are, of course, many types of recruiting programs. You must design a recruiting program that will work in your particular situation. Listed here are some of the possible activities which you may utilize. Refer to the "Bibliography" (score page 180) for further sources which explain recruiting activities and give additional ideas.

LETTER OR BROCHURE TO PARENTS

Somewhere in the recruiting plan, information about the beginning instrumental music program should be sent to parents. This may be done in a number of ways and formats. It may be a simple one-page letter or a colorful, elaborate printed brochure. It should include the following information:

1) Who may join.
2) How to join.
3) How to secure an instrument.
4) When classes meet.
5) Information regarding the Instrument Demonstration Program or Parents' Meeting.

Many times this letter or brochure includes a form or tear-off sheet so that an interested student may indicate a choice of instrument.

NEWSPAPER ARTICLES

Many directors place ads or articles in the local newspapers to inform members of the community of the beginning instrumental music program. A schedule of parent meetings, a photograph of a recruiting demonstration or students preparing for some performing activity and general information regarding the program may be included.

EVALUATION OF PROSPECTIVE STUDENTS

In elementary schools the classroom teacher is an excellent source of information and insight into the achievement levels and attitudes of prospective instrumental music students. Many teachers are delighted to be asked to provide verbal or written evaluations of prospective music students.

Although many directors do not use this information in selecting students for instrumental music programs, the cumulative files of students, kept in the school office, can be a good source for obtaining past records of prospective students.

MUSICAL APTITUDE TESTS

The validity of musical aptitude tests in evaluating a student's sense of rhythm, pitch and tonal memory has been a subject of debate among music education authorities for many years. Administering an aptitude test to all eligible students takes much time and effort. Many instrumental music programs have been successful without using these tests. If you decide to use an aptitude test, be careful that it encourages rather than frightens students away from the music program and that it does not prevent highly motivated students from participating in instrumental music classes.

If you do give musical aptitude tests to prospective students, the tests may be utilized in several different ways:

1) As an important factor in evaluating and selecting students for the program.
2) As a tool for generating interest. Test results create curiosity and gain attention of both students and parents.
3) As a possible method of identifying talented pupils who can be encouraged to join the instrumental music program.
4) As a guide to help in assisting students to particular instruments.

SELECTION AND FOLLOW-UP

After the entire evaluation process has been completed, students usually are sent written invitations to join the instrumental music program. Included in these letters should be the name of the recommended string instrument, information about securing an instrument, the title of the method book, the date of the first class, and a schedule of classes. The local music dealers normally are delighted to cooperate with you to assure an ample supply of instruments and method books. It is important that you follow-up on students who receive high evaluations but do not attend the first class meeting. Many fine students have become part of an instrumental music program because the teacher cared enough to encourage them to join.

BIBLIOGRAPHY

Dillon, Jacquelyn A. and Casimer Kriechbaum, Jr. *How to Design and Teach a Successful School String and Orchestra Program.* San Diego, CA.: Kjos West, 1978.

Fink, Lorraine. *A Parent's Guide to String Instrument Study.* San Diego, CA.: Neil A. Kjos Music Company, 1977.

Galamian, Ivan. *Principles of Violin Playing and Teaching.* Englewood Cliffs, N.J.: Prentice-Hall, 1962.

Kievman, Louis. *Practicing the Viola Mentally-Physically.* Pacific Palisades, CA.: Kelton Publications, 1969.

Krolick, Edward. "Basic Principles of Double Bass Playing." Reston, Virginia: Music Educators National Conference, 1957.

Lamb, Norman. *Guide to Teaching Strings.* Dubuque, IA.: William C. Brown, 1981.

Lorrin, Mark. *Dictionary of Bowing and Tonal Techniques for Strings.* Denver, CO.: Charles Hansen Educational Music and Books, 1968.

Mantel, Gerhard. *Cello Technique.* Bloomington, IN.: Indiana University Press, 1972.

Matesky, Ralph, and Ralph E. Rush. *Playing and Teaching Stringed Instruments,* Part 1 and 2. Englewood Cliffs, N.J.: Prentice-Hall, 1964.

Oddo, Vincent. *Playing and Teaching the Strings.* Belmont, CA.: 2 Wadsworth, 1979.

Potter, Louis Alexander. *The Art of Cello Playing: A Complete Textbook for Private or Class Instruction.* Evanston, IL.: Summy-Birchard, 1964.

Rolland, Paul and Marla Mutschler. *The Teaching of Action in String Playing, Development and Remedial Techniques.* Urbana, IL.: Illinois String Research Associates, 1974.

Scherl and Roth, Inc. *You Fix Them.* Cleveland, OH.: 1955.

Skoldberg, Phyllis. *The Strings, A Comparative View.* Bloomington, IN.: Frangpani Press, 1982.

Stanfield, Milly B. *The Intermediate Cellist.* London, England: Oxford University Press, 1973

Starr, William. *The Suzuki Violinist.* Knoxville, TN.: Kingston Ellis Press, 1976.

Turetzky, Bertram. *The Contemporary Contrabass.* Berkeley, CA.: University of California Press, 1974.

Young, Phyllis. *Playing the String Game: Strategies for Teaching Cello and Strings.* Austin, TX.: University of Texas Press, 1978.